Other Titles of Interest

REMOTE CONTROL HANDBOOK

by
OWEN BISHOP

BERNARD BABANI (publishing) LTD
THE GRAMPIANS
SHEPHERDS BUSH ROAD
LONDON W6 7NF
ENGLAND

Please Note

Although every care has been taken with the production of this book to ensure that any projects, designs, modifications and/or programs etc. contained herewith, operate in a correct and safe manner and also that any components specified are normally available in Great Britain, the Publishers and Author do not accept responsibility in any way for the failure, including fault in design, of any project, design, modification or program to work correctly or to cause damage to any other equipment that it may be connected to or used in conjunction with, or in respect of any other damage or injury that may be so caused, nor do the Publishers accept responsibility in any way for the failure to obtain specified components.

Notice is also given that if equipment that is still under warranty is modified in any way or used or connected with home-built equipment then that warranty may be void.

© 1988 BERNARD BABANI (publishing) LTD

First Published — September 1988
Reprinted — December 1990
Reprinted — June 1992

British Library Cataloguing in Publication Data:
Bishop, O.
    Remote control handbook.
    1. Remote control electronic equipment.
    Project - Amateurs' manuals
    I. Title
    621.381

    ISBN 0 85934 185 2

Printed and Bound in Great Britain by Cox & Wyman Ltd., Reading

Warning

Certain circuits and projects included in this book involve mains voltages and wiring. These are not recommended for beginners or those with little knowledge or experience of working with mains wiring and voltages.

Foreword

Ever since the predecessor of this book, *Remote Control Projects* (BP73) was published in 1980, there has been continuous interest in it from electronics enthusiasts and from workers in various fields, who have serious applications for remote control technology. Now, in response to this interest, we produce a completely new book on the subject. In doing this, we have retained some of the well-tried and tested circuits, especially the simpler ones which beginners have found easy to construct and use. At the same time, we have checked that the components specified for them are still available today.

In addition, this book contains improved and updated versions of some of the previous circuits. As well as this we have added a number of completely new circuits that have not been published before. Many of these are concerned with aspects of remote control that have increased in importance during the last few years. In particular, there are circuits for interfacing microcomputers to remote control systems, for using fibre-optics, and for using the domestic mains wiring system as transmission links. There are new circuits for stepper motors, voltage-to-frequency conversion and frequency-to-voltage conversion.

The book provides circuit diagrams, together with full explanations of how they work, testing and fault-finding. Appendix A gives full pin-out diagrams of all semiconductors and integrated circuits used in the book. We do not give stripboard diagrams or printed circuit board layouts since the exact requirements for these depend so much upon the application. Readers who are new to electronics construction should refer to one or more of the books listed in Appendix B. The book is, of course, restricted to the *electronic* aspects of remote control, assuming that readers are already familiar with the *mechanical* aspects of the devices they wish to control.

As is explained in the next chapter, remote control systems lend themselves to a modular approach. This makes it possible for a wide range of systems, from the simplest to the most complex, to be built up from a number of relatively simple modules. We have tried to ensure that, as far as possible, the circuit modules in this book are compatible with one another. They can be linked together in many different configurations to produce remote control systems tailored to individual requirements. Whether you wish simply to switch a table lamp on and off, to control a flying model aircraft, or to operate an industrial robot, we hope that this book will provide the circuits you require.

Owen Bishop

Contents

Chapter 1

REMOTE CONTROL SYSTEMS

What is remote control?

In *remote control*, an *operator* (perhaps you) exercises control over a *controlled device* without actually being in direct contact with it. The parts of a remote control system are shown in Figure 1.1. The essential features are:

1. The operator has a *transmitter*, which produces *code signals*.
2. The signals are transmitted through a *transmission link*.
3. The signals are picked up by a *receiver*.
4. The receiver sends *control signals* to the controlled device.

As an example, take the remote-control system of a TV set. The operator is you. The transmitter is the hand-held device that you point at the TV set when you want to change channels, increase the sound volume, or in some other way affect the action of the set. The transmission link is the infra-red light emitted by the transmitter, some of which reaches the receiver. The receiver, which usually is situated in a panel at the front of the TV set, sends control signals to the appropriate parts of the TV set. The TV set responds to your remote command.

Note the three types of signal involved in this sequence. The command signal is your means of putting instructions into the system. This is often done by pressing a button. Also there are systems in which the operator is not a person, but a computer. Then the command signal is a series of electrical pulses, generated by the computer. The code signal is usually a series of pulses, either electrical pulses, light pulses, ultrasonic pulses, or pulses of some other kind, depending on the nature of the transmission link. A different series of pulses is generated for each command. Finally, the control signal is the one which actually makes the controlled device perform as expected. It is usually electrical, switching on relays, lamps or motors.

1

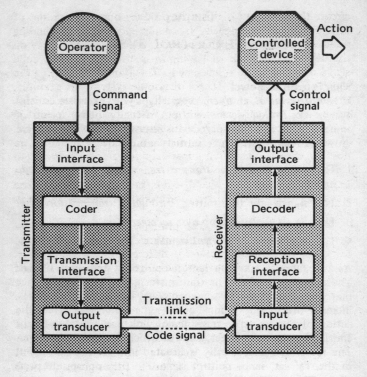

Fig. 1.1 The parts of a remote control system.

Transmitters

The function of the transmitter is to accept the command signal and generate the corresponding coded signal. Figure 1.1 shows that there are several distinct parts to the transmitter. The command signal is received by the *input interface*. This often consists of a switch or push-button, which is either 'on' or 'off'. There may sometimes be several such switches or buttons, one for each command signal. For example, a TV controller has individual buttons for changing channel, increasing volume, decreasing volume, increasing brightness, and so on. The next stage in the transmitter is the *coder circuit* the function of this is to produce one of a number of different electrical signals, (sequence of pulses) depending upon which button is being pressed. We have more to say on the different methods of coding in later chapters. The code signal now has to be transmitted. This is done by sending the signal to a *transducer*. In an ultrasonic system, for example, the transducer is a crystal specially cut to oscillate at high frequency, usually at 40kHz. When a suitable electrical signal is applied to the crystal it emits sound waves at 40kHz. In short, the transducer converts an electrical signal to an ultrasonic one. The transducer requires a special circuit to drive it, which we refer to as the *transmission interface*. This receives electrical code signals from the coder and causes the transducer to produce the corresponding signals in ultrasound.

In an infra-red system, the principle is just the same, but here the transducer is a light-emitting diode, operating in the infra-red band. This requires a different transmission interface circuit designed to make the diode emit pulses of infra-red radiation.

Transmission link

This may simply be 'space', across which an electromagnetic signal (visible light, infra-red, radio) passes from the transmitter to the receiver. Remote control of space-craft depends upon this type of link, using radio signals. Though there is air in the room in which your TV operates, the infra-red signal passing from the controller to the set could pass equally well in the absence of air. This does not apply to an ultrasonic system, which requires air, or some other physical medium, for transmission.

Noise

Before going further we must consider the subject of noise. We can define noise as an unwanted signal that somehow or other gets into the system. If the noise signal is sufficiently large compared with the signal we are trying to transmit, it may prove impossible for the system to function properly (Fig. 1.2). Noise can be introduced into the system at any stage. It might, for example, be caused by a faulty or poorly

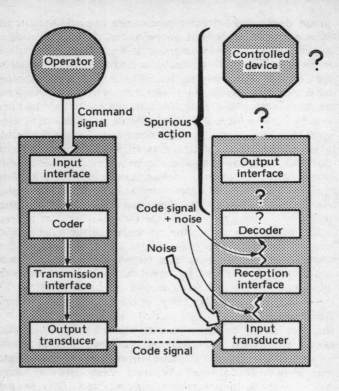

Fig. 1.2 Noise enters the system.

designed push-button, which generates multiple and irregular input pulses instead of just one 'clean' pulse when it is pushed. Good mechanical design of the switch, and special features of the input interface circuit can usually prevent such noise from being a serious problem. Noise can also be introduced when an electrical circuit is influenced by magnetic fields originating from nearby electrical equipment. The magnetic fields from a TV tube can induce spurious currents in electronic circuits, and seriously interfere with their operation. In this way, noise could be introduced into the remote control system at the decoder or transmission interface stage. However, with good circuit design and by taking precautions to shield the circuits from magnetic fields, it is normally easy to prevent noise in these circuits. The transmission link is the point at which noise is most likely to be introduced. In an infra-red system, for example, there may be several other sources of infra-red radiation that can produce spurious signals. Incandescent lamps, sunlight, heaters, other infra-red control devices and various other sources can interfere with transmission, or even saturate the receiver so that the code signals are lost altogether. The same applies with radio transmission, as any listener to the short-wave bands will have experienced. As with radio, several types of remote control system employ a kind of 'tuning'. Only a receiver operating with the correct frequency can receive the signal. This does not prevent noise from interfering with the signal, as on AM radio, but it does at least allow several separate systems to operate in the same locality without mutual interference.

There are several techniques for minimising the effects of noise. One is to repeat the signal until it has been correctly received. If you hold down one of the buttons on the TV controller (and assuming that your controller has a red *visible* light emitting diode to indicate that a signal is being sent), you will see that it is flashing with a repeating pattern of pulses. When you see the set respond, by changing channel for example, you release the button. In the meantime the signal may have been sent dozens of times. Some sets may emit a 'bleep' when a valid signal has been received. On other sets there is light-emitting diode that comes on to indicate this.

Another method of avoiding noise is to screen the receiver so that it can receive signals only from a narrow angle. The transmitter must then be placed within this angle, which may limit the conditions under which the system can be used.

The remarks above apply to open systems, in which the receiver is able to detect emissions from any sources in the locality. Although such systems are susceptible to noise, they have the advantage of flexibility in the positioning of transmitter and receiver. In a TV control system, you can control the set from almost anywhere in the room. Similarly, a flying model aircraft can be controlled from any position on the ground, within the range of the transmitter. By contrast a closed system has a physical transmission link running from transmitter to receiver. An example is an optical fibre link. A filament of special optical fibre runs from the transmitter to the receiver. Signals (visible or infra-red light) passed into one end of the fibre, emerge from the other end with relatively little loss of intensity and almost complete freedom from noise. This is because the outer coatings of the fibre prevent light entering the fibre except at its connection to the transmitter. This connection is made completely proof against external light sources, so eliminating noise. The disadvantage of this system is the physical connection between the transmitter and receiver. For example such a system is not suitable for controlling a mobile robot.

Receiver

To a certain extent the parts of the receiver are the same as those of the transmitter, but in reverse. The code signal is received by an input transducer. This converts the code signal into an electric signal. An ultrasonic crystal, if caused to vibrate by an incoming ultrasound of the correct frequency, produces electrical currents. A photo-cell detects pulses of light arriving at its surface and produces a correspondingly pulsing electric current. Currents flow in a radio antenna in response to radio signals arriving at it.

Unless the transmission link is closed (e.g. optical fibre or wired connection) the signal arriving at the receiver is very weak compared with that being transmitted. The greater the transmission distance the weaker the signal. Thus it is nearly always necessary for the received signal to be amplified electronically before anything else can be done with it. If noise is present, this is amplified too, though there are techniques for reducing the effects of this. Any amplifying circuit generates a certain amount of noise within itself so, if reliable operation is required over long distances, special low-noise amplifiers must be used. We shall come across examples of these later in the book. The task of the reception interface is to amplify the incoming code signal. Even with amplification, the incoming signal may lack the sharpness of the original transmitted signal (Fig. 1.3). Pulses that were initially square may have come distorted and jagged. The reception interface

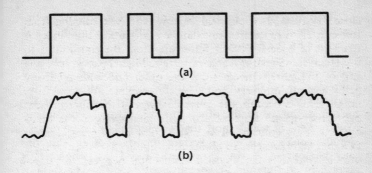

Fig. 1.3 (a) Original square–wave signal.
(b) Signal degraded by distortion and noise.

may therefore include circuits to restore the original square shape to the pulses before passing them on to the decoder.

The task of the decoder is to recognise the code signal and pass the corresponding control signal to the output interface. For example if you have pressed the 'change channels' button, then a particular code signal is transmitted and received. On receiving this particular signal, the decoder causes the output interface to activate that part of the TV set concerned with changing channels. The decoder circuit can help with the problem of noise, if it is designed so as to respond only to those signals which have particular characteristics. Thus the controller uses a given set of signals, which is different to the set used by the video player. Both devices can be controlled independently in the same room.

Types of command

If the transmitter has a single press-button or switch, there are only two possible commands, 'button pressed' and 'button not pressed'. This is a very simple system which would be adequate for operating a lamp, or detonating an explosive charge. In such a system the button or switch is either 'on' or 'off'. The system is termed a *binary* system because of its two states. In a binary system there is no need to have a coder or decoder stage. When the button is pressed the output interface is activated directly, to generate a continuous signal. When this reaches the input interface, the input interface communicates directly with the controlled device to activate it.

The next most complicated type of command is that in which one of several different buttons is pressed. The TV controller is an example of this. Each button is either 'pressed' or 'not pressed', and at any one time one of the buttons is 'on' while the others are 'off'. It is also possible to have systems in which more than one button might be pressed simultaneously. In either system the state of the buttons may be represented by a row of 1's and 0's, where '1' is equivalent to 'on' and '0' is equivalent to 'off'. The state of 8 buttons could be represented by 8 binary digits, like this:

$$00100000$$

Conventionally, the digit on the right (the least significant digit, if we consider this to be an 8-digit binary number) represents button 0. The digit on the left (the most significant digit) represents button 7. In the number shown above, button 5 is pressed, while the others are not pressed. The states of the buttons are represented by the digits of a binary number, so this is a *digital* control system. Obviously, a coder is needed in this system, to produce a different sequence of pulses for each of the valid binary numbers.

A flying model aircraft, and certain types of robot may be controlled by using a joystick. The simpler types of joystick operate a number of switches, usually 4. When the joystick is in the vertical position, all switches are off (0000). One or two of the four switches are turned on when the stick is pushed in a given direction. For example, switch 0 may be turned on when the stick is pushed forward (0001), and switch 1 may be switched on when it is pushed to the left (0010). If the stick is pushed forward *and* to the left, switches 0 and 1 are on (0011). A joystick of this type is just a variant of the multiple push-button and gives a digital signal. Some versions, particularly those used with microcomputers have a fifth switch, the 'fire button'.

Joysticks of the type described above are not suitable for fine control. It may not be enough to command an aircraft to 'dive' or 'climb'. We need to be able to command it to 'dive very slightly' or 'climb very steeply'. We need to be able to *quantify* the command. In fact, as far as climbing is concerned, we need to be able to command the craft to climb at *any* angle from the smallest perceptible angle, to the steepest angle of which it is capable. A quantity that varies *smoothly* over a given range is known as an *analogue* quantity. The extent to which we want the craft to climb is indicated by the extent to which the joystick is pulled back from its central position. Attached to the joystick column is a rotary variable resistor (or potentiometer), the resistance of which is varied within a given range, according to how much the stick is moved from its central position (Fig. 1.4). Usually there are two such resistors, one for forward and backward movement and one for side to side movement.

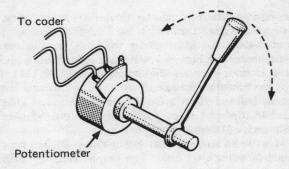

Fig. 1.4 Converting the position of a joystick into the analogous current.

In action, a current flows through the resistors, and the strength of the current through each resistor depends on its resistance, which in turn depends upon the position of the stick. The strength of the current is an analogue of the position of the stick. The problem is how to transmit this analogue information. With a direct wired connection this is easy since the current is sent along a wire directly to the controlled device. There it drives flight motors connected to the flight control surfaces of the aircraft. The stronger the current, the greater the deflection of the control surfaces. This arrangement will not work for an open system. For example, we *could* make an ultrasonic transmitter, in which the more the joystick is moved from its central position, the 'louder' the ultrasound. Unfortunately, the volume of sound at a given point is affected by reflections from nearby objects, and by the distance from the source of sound. Furthermore, we could not guarantee the precise performance of the amplifiers involved in producing the original signal, and in amplifying the received signal. These reasons make it impossible for the receiver to determine the original volume of transmitted sound. Transmitting an analogue quantity as an analogue signal is therefore a very unreliable technique.

The best solution to the problem of transmitting an analogue quantity is to convert it into a digital quantity first. In the ultra-sound example, silence would be represented by the 8-bit binary number 00000000 (= 0 in decimal). The maximum sound volume would be represented by 11111111 (= 255 in decimal). Sounds of intermediate volume would be represented by values between 00000000 and 11111111. Having converted the value to its digital form, we have an 8-digit value to transmit. This has 256 possible values (0 to 255), so we need a coder that produces one of 256 possible pulse sequences for each value. A very straightforward way to do this would be to transmit a pulse for every '1' but no pulse for every '0' (Fig. 1.5).

Readers may object that, having converted the analogue value into a digital one, we have lost the essential nature of analogue values. This is their ability to take any one of an *infinite* number of values within the prescribed range. These represent the smooth movement of the joystick, in infinitely small stages, from its fully forward position to its fully backward position. Instead, the 8-bit number has only 256 possible values. It is as if the joystick's smooth action is replaced by 256 'click-steps'. For most purposes, this difference is of no consequence. Given that the total angular travel of the joystick is about 70°, one step in the binary range represents an angular movement of the stick of only 0.27°. This action is 'smooth' enough for most applications. However, if greater precision is essential, we can resort to converting the analogue quantity into a 12-digit binary number. This gives us 4096 steps from 000000000000 to 111111111111. One step is equivalent to an angular change of only 0.017° in the position of the stick.

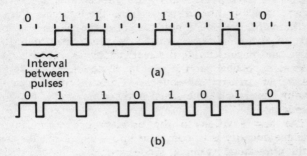

Fig. 1.5 Two ways of coding the number 01101010
for transmission as a series of pulses:
(a) pulse absent = 0; pulse present = 1:
(b) short pulse = 0; long pulse = 1.

Converting analogue quantities to digital quantities may sound complicated but, it is surprisingly easy in practice. This is because several types of integrated circuit have been designed just for this purpose. They are called *analogue-to-digital converters*. Sometimes they are referred to as *A-to-D converters*, for short. They are easy to use. The analogue signal is fed into one terminal of the i.c., and the corresponding digital output is obtained from 8 (or 12) output terminals. These outputs may then be fed to the coder. The reverse process is required in the receiver. The decoder produces an 8-bit digital value which is converted to an analogue signal by a *digital-to-analogue (D-to-A) converter* i.c. The analogue output from this, usually a voltage varying between 0V and 1.2V, is then fed to the controlled device. Here it may be used for such purposes as varying the speed of a motor, or determining the position of a servo-mechanism, or varying the

11

brightness of a TV picture. Since the input to the D-to-A converter has 256 possible values from 0 to 255, the so-called analogue output can not be a truly analogue quantity. The voltage actually takes one of 256 stepped values between 0V and 1.2V. Thus each step is only 4.7mV away from those on either side of it and, for all practical purposes this is an analogue quantity.

Chapter 2

TRANSMISSION LINKS

Several of the transmission links have already been mentioned briefly in Chapter 1. In this chapter we examine each in detail. Very often the choice of transmission link is the first stage in designing a remote control system. This is because each type of link has its own special features, suiting it for certain applications. We consider these features in this chapter. To make selections easier, the transmission links are divided according to the circumstances under which they can be used.

In the same room

This includes links that can be used at distances up to about 10 metres, and where communication between the transmitter and receiver is either direct or by reflection from the walls or ceiling of the room.

Ultra-sound

Ultra-sound is sound of high frequency, or pitch. Its pitch is too high to be heard by the human ear, though dogs and certain other animals are sensitive to it. Ultra-sound is usually generated by using a crystal that has its surfaces ground so that it vibrates at a frequency of 40kHz. To make the crystal vibrate we apply an oscillating potential across it. If the frequency of the oscillator is exactly 40kHz, the crystal resonates in phase with the applied oscillating potential, and ultra-sound is generated.

Ultra-sound is detected by the reverse process. The detector is a crystal similar to the generator crystal. Its surfaces are ground so that it vibrates at a frequency of 40kHz. When ultra-sound of the correct frequency falls on this crystal, the crystal resonates and begins to vibrate at the same frequency. Its vibrations generate an oscillating potential difference between opposite surfaces of the crystal. This potential is detected by suitable circuitry.

The advantages of ultra-sound are that the crystals are inexpensive and that the circuits required to generate the oscillating potential, and to detect the oscillations of the receiver crystal, are simple to construct and operate. A system using ultra-sound is therefore a good one for a beginner to construct as an introduction to remote control systems.

The wavelength of ultra-sound at 40kHz is a little less than 8mm. This is far less than the wavelength of the sounds contained in the human voice, which average 2 metres or more. Most of the sounds of everyday life have wavelengths well over 1 metre.

Since the furniture and other objects in a room (including people) have dimensions that are generally smaller than the wavelengths of everyday sounds, the sound waves are diffracted around such objects when they meet them. The objects do not cast any 'sound shadow'. If someone stands between you and the radio, you can still hear the broadcast well; if you are hiding behind a tree you can be heard when you sneeze. Similarly, sounds are *diffracted* when they come to an opening that is smaller than their wavelength. Sounds made inside a room pass through an open doorway or window and can be heard outside. You do not need to be able to *see* a person who is talking in a room to be able to *hear* that person quite plainly.

Ultra-sound is also diffracted by objects or openings as small as or smaller than its wavelength. Since people, furniture and many other objects have dimensions far greater than 8mm, they cast distinct *sound shadows*. If a person stands between the ultra-sonic transmitter and receiver, the transmission is blocked. Even a hand placed between them can prevent the transmission. It is important to remember this when using ultra-sound for remote control. Though you may be able to hear the sounds made by the model, the receiver in the model may not be able to hear the ultra-sound from the transmitter. If you wish to transmit ultra-sound from room to room, you must have an open 'line-of-sight' between transmitter and receiver. An alternative is to place a smooth reflective surface at the doorway to catch and redirect the beam from the transmitter.

The main disadvantage of ultra-sonic control is that the

range of control is normally limited to a few metres. The sound emitted by the crystal is confined to a relatively narrow beam. As with the sound from a treble loudspeaker, the beam does not spread appreciably. Similarly, the receiving crystal has a fairly narrow angle of acceptance. The effect is that the transmitter needs to be aimed fairly accurately at the receiver and to be within its angle of acceptance. For many applications this is no problem and can be an advantage. Although it is not normally affected by noise (using the term in the sense described in Chapter 1), certain sounds have brief ultra-sonic components and may cause spurious action on occasions.

Infra-red

This is one of the most popular techniques for domestic use. The infra-red radiation is generated by one or more light-emitting diodes (LEDs). They are cheap, have low current consumption, low failure rate, and the circuitry for driving them is simple. There are several devices suitable for detecting infra-red, though the most generally used is an inexpensive photodiode with enhanced sensitivity in the infra-red band. Circuitry of short range systems is simple and within the scope of the beginner. The range of operation is usually limited to a few metres though, in principle, a bank of ten or more LEDs working in parallel could be used to extend the range for use outdoors. There could be problems of noise from other sources of infra-red (e.g. the Sun) under such circumstances, unless precautions were taken to limit the angle of acceptance of the receiver by using a long tubular hood.

Visible light

This is an alternative to infra-red that is suitable for use in a room. See later in this chapter for further comments.

Wire

This is the easiest and cheapest transmission link of all. A pair of wires run from the coder of the transmitter to the decoder of the receiver. One wire is for 'ground' connection (0V), the other carries the signal. The prime disadvantage is that there has to be a physical connection to the controlled device. If this has to be mobile a wired connection may be out of the question.

Using a wired connection might seem to be almost equivalent to wiring the control panel directly to the controlled device, but there is an important difference. Given a control panel with 20 buttons, for example, we would need 21 wires to join it to the controlled device. A multicored cable of this size is cumbersome and expensive. By using the coding and decoding techniques of remote control, we are able to reduce the number of connecting wires to only 2. In effect, the buttons 'share' the pair of wires because the decoder sends a different signal along the wire depending upon which button is pressed. It is feasible to carry this concept further, having two or more control panels and two or more controlled devices all sharing the same pair of wires. Each panel might produce the same set of codes or each could be allocated its distinct set of codes. Similarly, the decoders in each device can be designed so as to respond only to codes concerning that particular device.

An application of this idea is the control of a model railway. There can be a number of control panels located conveniently around the layout. Each locomotive, pair of points, turntable, and signal is an individually controlled device. Instead of a pair of wires, we use the rails themselves.

One of the chief advantages of a wired system is that noise is kept to a minimum. Only in an environment in which there is strong electro-magnetic activity is there likely to be any trouble. A workshop in which heavy-duty motors are continually being switched on or off, is less suitable for wired transmission. The same applies to a model railway system. Even so, a good coding and decoding system overcomes intermittent noise simply by repeating the transmission until the message is safely received.

In an adjacent room

The main consideration here is whether the operator needs to know whether the command has been received and acted on. Maybe this will not matter but, if it does, some kind of feedback is required from the controlled device. This can take the form of a second remote link, operating in the reverse direction. Suggested systems are described later in the book.

Wire

This has been discussed in the previous section. If the wire is several tens of metres long and the signal is being transmitted at high frequency, it may be necessary to employ a line driver to minimise distortion of the signal. Suitable devices are described later.

Mains wiring

This is an extension of the system described earlier. When a building already has a wiring system that goes to every room, it makes sense to use this as a transmission link, instead of installing a separate wiring system for the purpose. Since the controlled devices will probably require a mains power supply anyway, the device needs only to be plugged in to the mains, and is then able to receive coded signals along the mains supply. The great advantage of using the mains wiring is flexibility. If you need to re-locate the control panel or any of the controlled devices to other rooms, no rewiring is required. Just unplug the device from its socket and plug it into another socket elsewhere in the house.

An important consideration when using mains wiring is that the mains supply is noisy. There is the 50Hz signal of the AC mains frequency, plus innumerable spikes as equipment is switched on and off, not only in the house itself, but possibly in adjoining premises. This problem is overcome by the use of suitable coding and decoding circuits.

A difficulty confronting the beginner is that the circuits necessarily include sections connected to the mains supply. Precautions have to be taken to ensure that the circuits are safely constructed. There are also risks at the testing stages, if the enclosure has to be open for testing, so exposing parts of the circuit which are at mains voltage. However, provided sensible precautions are taken and strictly observed there need be no real danger on this score. **However these types of circuits are not recommended for the beginner.**

Optical fibre

For complete immunity from noise, the use of optical fibre is strongly recommended. The signal takes the form of pulses of infra-red or visible light. Local electromagnetic activity has no effect whatsoever on the signal while it is passing through the optical fibre. Signals can be transmitted over distances of 100m or more with little noise or distortion. As with a direct wire connection, there is the disadvantage that the mobility of the controlled device is severely restricted.

Optical cable and the components required for interfacing it to the electronic circuits are relatively expensive, though costs have fallen in recent years. It is best, therefore, to limit the use of optical fibre to those systems in which freedom from noise is essential. Another application for optical fibre is in a system in which total security is essential. Code signals can not be intercepted and decoded by any device other than that in the intended receiver.

Greater distances

Radio

For distances of several hundred metres ultra-sound and infra-red lack the power, optical fibre is usually too expensive and wired systems are often impracticable. Radio has considerable advantages. The remote control of flying model aircraft, vehicles, boats and mobile robots are frequently met examples. The radio transmitter and receiver are more expensive to construct (though not unduly so), more bulky and have a greater current consumption, but these are not insuperable problems. The construction and alignment of a radio transmitter and receiver require a little more expertise, but are within the scope of all except the absolute beginner.

As in many other systems, noise can be a problem. In a radio system, the commonest source of noise is other radio transmissions. Operators of flying model aircraft may experience interference from CB transmitters operating in the locality — particularly from passing cars and lorries. This has been known to cause the operator to lose control.

Visible light

A big advantage of using visible light as the transmission link is that the transmitter and receiver can be very simply constructed. Indeed, a cheap pocket torch will often act as a transmitter of the single-pulse kind. The great difficulty is that light abounds in the environment, especially by day, so that the transmissions may be subject to considerable interference. One way of reducing the interference problem is to transmit the light in a sharply-focused beam. The light is produced by a small filament-lamp, such as an ordinary torch-bulb, and is brought to a parallel-sided beam by a short-focus lens. This is directed at a similar device, with a light-sensitive transistor or phototransistor in place of the bulb. One advantage of this system is that control may be exercised over considerable distances — several tens of metres — but the receiver and transmitter must be visible to each other. For distances exceeding, say 20 metres, some care must be taken to align the transmitting and receiving devices, and they must be secured firmly against the effects of wind and weather, but once so adjusted, the system is reliable. It has practically no application to model control, except for fixed models, such as model machines, but can have applications for the remote control of many other kinds of electrically-powered device, such as pumps, greenhouse heaters and lights. They are especially useful where it is not permissible or convenient to run wires to carry the transmissions, for example, if a public road passes between transmitter and receiver.

Chapter 3

DIGITAL ELECTRONICS

Many of the circuits described in this book are digital electronic circuits. Before going further, it is important to be clear what is meant by this. Since digital electronics depends upon the binary number system, we must first look at what this is, as far as it applies to electronic circuits.

Binary numbers

Through the ages, several different systems have been invented for counting numbers of objects. The one that most people use today is the *decimal system*. In this system there are ten numeric symbols, 0 to 9, used to express values in the range 0 to 9. To express values greater than 9, we use the same ten symbols, but the value represented by a symbol depends upon its position within the string of digits representing the value. In other words, we have hundreds, tens and units and, for bigger values, thousands, tens of thousands and so on.

For example, the value 'two hundred and forty-four' is written in decimal notation as '244'. This example uses two of the ten numeric symbols, '2' and '4'. The '4' on the right represents 4 *units*. The next '4', being positioned second from the right, represents four *tens*, or forty. The '2', being positioned third from the right, represents two *hundreds*. Increasing the value of the left-most digit by 1 increases the value of the whole number by 100, an effect that is more significant than that of increasing either of the other two digits by 1. Therefore the '2', which occupies the left-most position is referred to as the *most significant digit*. We often use the abbreviation 'MSD' for this digit. The right-most digit is referred to as the *least significant digit*.

The same value written in binary notation is '11110100'. Only two symbols, '0' and '1' are used in the binary system. To express the value 'two' we use a position-dependent system, just as in the decimal system. The position, reading from the right, represents powers of two instead of powers of ten.

In the decimal form (244) the digits represent hundreds, tens, and units.

In the binary form (11110100) the digits represent one-hundred-and-twenty-eights, sixty-fours, thirty-twos, sixteens, eights, fours, twos and units.

Thus the binary value 11110100 is converted to decimal form like this, working from the right:

Decimal equivalent

The right-most '0' (LSD) means 'no units'	0
The next '0' means 'no twos'	0
The right-most '1' means 'one four'	4
The next '0' means 'no eights'	0
The next '1' means 'one sixteen'	16
The next '1' means 'one thirty-two'	32
The next '1' means 'one sixty-four'	64
The left-most '1' (MSD) means 'one one-hundred and twenty-eight'	128

Total value = 244

In general, when a value expressed is in binary it requires more digits than when it is expressed in decimal. So what is the advantage of using the binary system in electronic circuits? The next section explains this.

Binary circuits

In many electronic circuits, a part of the circuit may be in one of two distinct states. The circuit is such that no in-between states are possible. For example, a switch is either open or closed. It is not possible for the switch to be 'half-open' or 'half-closed'. We could represent the state of such a circuit by '0' if the circuit is open, or '1' if it is closed. Figure 3.1 shows a circuit that has 8 switches. Each one represents a digit of a binary value. The circuit is shown in the state which represents the binary value 11110100, equivalent to decimal 244. The value is represented not only by the states of the switches, but also by the states of the lamps.

22

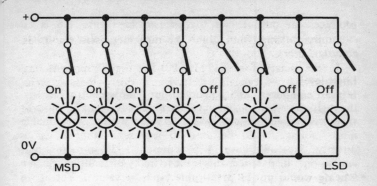

*Fig. 3.1 A simple way of representing the value 244
in digital form. ON = 1; OFF = 0.*

It might be argued that a lamp can be in one of many states
between fully off and fully on. It might possibly have a variable resistor in series with it. This situation can be resolved
by defining what we mean by 'on' and 'off'. We could say
that if the brightness of the lamp is below a given level the
lamp counts as 'off'. This includes the true fully off state
when no current flows through the lamp. If the lamp is
brighter than a certain level, it counts as 'on'. To make the
distinction between 'on' and 'off' clearer, there could be a
range of intermediate brightness which we count as neither
'on' nor 'off'. The circuit would be designed so that this
intermediate brightness could not normally occur. In this
way, a circuit that could possibly be in many intermediate
states is considered to have only two valid states. It is a binary
circuit.

Binary circuits are the basis of computers. Though numer-
ical values normally appear on the screen in decimal form,
this is only to make things easier for the human operator.
Within the computer itself all values are handled in binary
form. To represent values larger than 1 it is necessary to have
several circuits working in parallel, each one representing a
single digit. The circuit of Figure 3.1 is of this type. Another
way is to arrange for the output of the circuit to represent the
digits one after another, as a sequence of pulses. A circuit that

produces an output like that shown in Figure 1.5 is an example. Either type of circuit is known as a *digital electronic circuit*.

Logic levels

In most computers, and in many of our remote control circuits, the digits are represented by *voltage levels*. It might be thought that, since a voltage can take any value within a reasonable range, voltage could be used to represent numeric values directly. We could have 1V to represent 1, 2V to represent 2, and so on. In practice, this leads to many difficulties. Such a scheme would not be practicable for large values. Yet, if we were to scale the values down, so that 1V represents say 10,000, the difference between 1 and 2 is only 0.1mV. Circuits to produce or measure voltages with sufficient precision are very expensive to construct. To build something as complicated as a computer from such circuits would be prohibitively expensive. This is why computers are based on digital electronics. The circuits can be simple and cheap, yet are precise, extremely reliable and fast-acting.

Simplification and robustness of operation can be achieved if we do not require absolute precision in operation. We adopt the approach described in the example of lamp brightness, given earlier. We decide what voltage *range* shall represent '0' and what shall represent '1'. One of the more widely used types of digital circuit is known as TTL. This is short for *transistor-transistor logic*. Many of the circuits described in this book make use of TTL, since they can be built up quickly from ready-made and inexpensive unit circuits. These are available very cheaply as integrated circuits. TTL circuits use a standard 5V supply. Any voltage between 0V and 0.8V represents '0'. We usually refer to this as 'low'. Any voltage between 2V and 5V represents '1', and is referred to as 'high'. Voltages of intermediate level (0.8V to 2V) are not valid, and produce indeterminate results. Circuits must be designed so that such voltages can not occur. Given the wide range of voltages that *are* acceptable, this requirement presents no problems to the designer.

It is important to remember the valid TTL voltages when testing circuits that you have built. If you expect to find a 'high' voltage at a certain terminal, do not assume that it must necessarily be the full 5V of the supply. If your test measurement shows the voltage to be 3.75V, for example, this is valid as a 'high' voltage. Of course, if the voltage is only a little above 2V, it might happen that, under other operating conditions, the voltage could fall a little *below* 2V resulting in unreliable operation. Circuits in this book are designed not to produce voltages close to the permissible limits, so it would be worthwhile to check the connections carefully.

The standard operating voltage of TTL is 5V, which is the power supply voltage used for most of the circuits in a microcomputer. This voltage is not readily obtainable from a battery. This limits the usefulness of TTL in portable equipment, including much remote control equipment. However, most circuits employing TTL will also operate on a 6V supply, which may be obtained from four 1.5V cells connected in series. The operating voltage is supplied to the *collectors* of the bipolar transistors in the logic i.c.s. For this reason the supply rail is often referred to as V_{CC}.

The other main group of logic circuits used in this book is the CMOS family. This uses an operating voltage anywhere between 3V and 15V. Many of the circuits in this book use a 9V supply, because this is conveniently obtainable from a PP3 or similar 9V battery. The small physical size of the battery makes it ideal for use in hand-held equipment, such as controller units.

The current requirements of CMOS are less than that of the standard TTL (though there are low-power versions of TTL). This means that a small battery such as the PP3 has a long operating life with CMOS circuits. Owing to the nature of CMOS devices, output voltage levels are either close to 0V or close to the supply voltage. This 'all-or-nothing' feature lends itself to digital design, in which a voltage close to 0V represents '0' and a voltage close to the supply voltage represents '1'. The operating voltage is supplied to the drain electrodes of the field effect transistors in the logic i.c.s. For this reason the supply rail is often referred to as V_{DD}. The 0V rail, connected to the *source* electrodes is often referred to as V_{SS}.

While this book was in preparation, two new series of TTL

i.c.s became widely available. These are the 74HC and the 74HCT series, both of which are pin-compatible with standard TTL and so can be substituted for the standard (74 series) and low power (74LS series) i.c.s used in this book. The 74HC series is based on CMOS technology so it has the advantage of very low power requirements, an important consideration for battery-powered remote control. Its power requirements are considerably less even than that of the CMOS '4000' series, thus effecting even greater savings. Yet it does not have the disadvantage of the slow speed of the '4000' i.c.s. Although its fan-out (the number of gates its outputs can be fed to) is not as great as standard TTL, none of the circuits in this book require high fan-out, so this is not likely to be a design problem. The only point to bear in mind, if you are mixing standard and 74HC types in the same circuit, is that a 74HC output can supply only 2 standard TTL inputs. It can supply 10 low power TTL inputs, and an unlimited number of 74HC or '4000' series inputs.

Another 'plus' feature of the 74HC series is that it does not require the regulated +5V supply needed by standard TTL. It operates on any supply voltage in the range +2V to +6V. This too makes it very suitable for battery-powered applications.

Although the 74HC series has many points in its favour, there are some features that could be disadvantageous under certain circumstances. For one thing, it is CMOS-based and therefore needs the careful handling referred to on page 28. There is also the point that its input characteristics are not identical with those of standard and low power TTL. In other words, if you feed a standard or low power TTL output to a 74HC input terminal, the 74HC circuit *may* not differentiate correctly between 'low' and 'high'. It is therefore possible that some of the circuits in this book, especially those using TTL i.c.s as 'clocks', may not work in exactly the same way. If you are mixing TTL types in one circuit and have standard or low power TTL outputs going to 74HC inputs, connect the 74HC input to V_{CC} by a 4.7kΩ resistor. This acts as a pull-up resistor, raising the standard TTL high output level to that recognised by 74HC as a high input. If problems arise over these slightly different input characteristics of 74HC, the 74HCT series can be used. This has the same input character-

26

istics as standard TTL. The 74HCT series, however has a smaller power supply range, from 4.5V to 5.5V, though it probably works correctly on a 6V battery in most applications.

It is possible to use both TTL and CMOS i.c.s in the same circuit. This may be useful if i.c.s to provide all the functions required in a circuit are not all available in one family. It is easiest, though not essential, to operate both types of i.c. on the same supply voltage. TTL requires V_{CC} to be +5V (or +6V, for battery-powered equipment), and this is suitable for the V_{DD} rail for CMOS.

The input and output characteristics of TTL and CMOS do not match. Figure 3.2 shows how to connect an output from one type to an input of the other type.

The main disadvantage of CMOS is that the i.c.s are susceptible to damage by stray electro-static charges. Though the manufacturers protect the i.c.s by incorporating diodes to short-circuit externally applied charges, it is wise to eliminate the risk of damage by observing these few precautions when handling CMOS i.c.s:

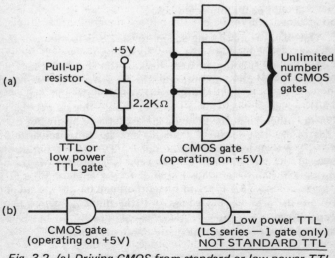

Fig. 3.2 (a) Driving CMOS from standard or low power TTL
(b) Driving low power TTL from CMOS

27

(i)   Suppliers usually send the i.c. to you with its terminal pins shorted together by metal foil or conductive foam (black); leave the i.c. in this packing until you are ready to use it.

(ii) Carry out all construction work on an earthed metal surface. The author uses an inverted lid from an old biscuit 'tin'.

(iii) Do not wear clothes made from synthetic fibre when handling CMOS i.c.s for these are liable to generate electrostatic charges. Preferably roll up your sleeves and rest your wrist or forearm on the metal sheet when handling the i.c.s.

(iv) Earth the bit of the soldering iron.

(v)   Touch other metal tools (wire-strippers, screwdrivers, etc.) against the metal sheet to discharge them immediately before use.

(vi) Build the circuit without i.c.s, then solder the i.c.s last.

(vii) When testing partly-built circuits, the power supply to the i.c. must be on before high inputs are applied to other pins. When testing is completed, the power supply should be disconnected last.

One way of minimising danger to the i.c. is to mount it in a socket. The circuit is built first, including the socket for the i.c. When all is complete and checked, the i.c. can be inserted in the socket, observing precautions (i), (ii) and (iii) as listed above. Using sockets simplifies the procedure and makes it much easier to remove the i.c. later should this be necessary. On the other hand, the price of the socket may be greater than that of the i.c., so direct soldering and careful observance of all the precautions can save money. The use of pin strips instead of conventional i.c. sockets is a satisfactory compromise for those who do not wish to risk soldering the i.c.s directly to the circuit board. The beginner should not be put off by the grim warnings above. Using the above procedure, and even with occasional careless lapses, the author has never damaged any i.c. among the many hundreds handled.

Chapter 4

METHODS OF CONTROL

In this chapter we deal with the various methods of coding command signals. It is essential to consider these before designing a system in detail.

As Figure 4.1 illustrates, there are five main methods of control.

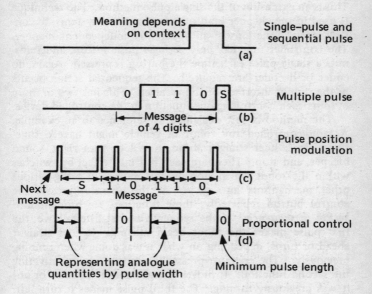

Fig. 4.1 Waveforms of various types of control signal.
S = synchronising pulse or interval.

Single pulse

A single pulse (a burst of ultra-sound, for example, or a flash of radiation from an infra-red LED), triggers a single response. The effect can be a true trigger in that the action continues after the pulse has ended. For example, the pulse triggers a lamp to switch on. It stays on after the pulse is ended. Alternatively, the lamp remains on only for as long as the pulse continues.

This is by far the simplest method of remote control, and is adequate for many purposes. The controller unit requires only a single push-button. No coding or decoding are required since the pulse itself conveys all the necessary information.

Sequential pulse

This is an extension of the single pulse method. The technique is used in the cheaper kind of remote control systems, to control several functions in an apparently independent manner. The controller unit has only a single push-button, and transmits a single pulse each time the button is pressed. Again, no coder or decoder are required. The sequential action occurs in the output interface of the receiver. This has two or more outputs each controlling one function in the controlled device.

The method is best explained by reference to an example. A radio-controlled toy robot or vehicle might have 6 functions: start, steer straight ahead, turn left, turn right, sound bleeper, and stop. These are each put into effect by switches within the robot which stop or start motors or bring various other mechanisms into play. As the operator presses the control button repeatedly, these functions are brought into action *in sequence*. If the sequence is that listed above, the first pulse makes the robot begin moving. It goes straight ahead or turns, depending on what it was doing when running previously. The operator presses the button again, activating the second function. It moves straight ahead, whether or not it was previously turning. The third pulse makes it turn left. If the operator wants it to turn right instead, pulse 3 is quickly followed by pulse 4, so that the robot has no time to make an effective response to pulse 3. The robot responds to the pulse in sequence, but the operator makes it skip over the unwanted functions by pressing the button again immediately. The robot continues turning right. To stop it turning right four more pulses in quick succession, make it skip the 'bleeper', 'stop' and 'start' functions and bring the 'straight ahead' function into action.

This method of control may sound cumbersome, as it certainly is if there are many functions in the sequence, but has the merit of simplicity. With a few functions, perhaps eight as a maximum, the circuits are easy to build and to use.

The simplest form of sequential control is the *toggle action*. There are only 2 steps in the sequence. A lamp, for example, is switched on when the first pulse arrives. It remains on until the next pulse arrives. The effect is exactly like that of the push-on/push-off switches often found on domestic lighting equipment. There are many applications for this type of control.

Multiple pulse

This method is used when the functions of the controlled device are such that skipping quickly through some of them is not feasible. Or it may be that there are so many functions that it would take too long to run through the sequence each time a new function is to be brought into action. With this system each function is controlled entirely independently of the rest. The controller usually has several buttons or keys, one for each function. There is a coder to generate a series of coded pulses. In the relatively simple multiple-pulse coder described in this book, the series of pulses begins with a short synchronising pulse (Fig. 4.1b). This alerts the decoder in the receiver to the fact that a series of pulses is about to arrive. During the next four pulse intervals, high or low pulses are received. These constitute the coded signal. Thus any binary number in the range 0000 to 1111 (0 to 15 in decimal) can be transmitted, giving a maximum of 16 different codes. After decoding, up to 16 different functions can be activated, which is more than enough for most applications. A model railway locomotive might use the following: forward, reverse, stop, slow speed, medium speed, high speed, lights on, lights off, sound whistle. This still leaves 7 functions available for the ingenious modeller to use for other purposes.

Pulse position modulation

In this system the pulses are all of equal length. The intervals *between* the pulses are varied to convey the coded information. In this book we use a system based on a proprietary i.c. The pulse train consists of 6 pulses (Fig. 4.1c), allowing a coded message of 5 binary digits, and a synchronising interval. This i.c. is designed for controlling devices such as TV sets. The keyboard has up to 21 keys. The system allows for a number of functions, including three analogue outputs. On a TV set these would be used for controlling volume, brightness and contrast, but they are equally applicable to the controlling of the speed of motors. Further details are given in the sections dealing with using these i.c.s.

Analogue control

There are two approaches to analogue control. In one, of which the PPM system described above is an example, an analogue output of the decoder is at a fixed voltage when first switched on. A motor connected to such an output always begins running at a fixed speed. Then the command given is either to increase or to decrease the analogue output. The output is accordingly stepped up or down to its maximum or minimum value. The multiple-pulse system can also be used to produce a similar action by allocating one code to 'step up' and another to 'step down'. This technique is simple and reliable. To give a reasonably fine control requires a minimum of 32 steps, and each step takes an appreciable time to occur. To step from one extreme to the other can be unacceptably slow. However, for many purposes, such as altering the sound volume of a TV set, a slow rate of change is an asset.

The other approach to analogue control allows instantaneous changes in the analogue output and a fine degree of control. In this system (Fig. 4.1d), pulses are sent at regular intervals but the *length* of the pulse is varied in proportion to the analogue quantity being transmitted. This is known as the *proportional control* method. The pulse length can be varied smoothly between its minimum and maximum, so a true analogue control is obtainable. Since the system normally requires two time-dependent circuits, one in the transmitter and one in the receiver, it is difficult to ensure that a given input to the transmitter (e.g. joystick position) will result in accurate response (e.g. rudder position) in the controlled device. If there is some kind of feedback (the operator can see the controlled device), this presents no problem. An advantage of the system is that the circuits required are relatively simple.

A more serious trouble that may affect the proportional control is noise. This can alter the apparent length of the pulse, so introducing error into the system, when the receiving circuits try to measure the pulse length. Response is erratic. One way round this is to convert the analogue quantity into digital form before coding. A multiple pulse system is then used to transmit the digital value. A 4-digit multiple pulse system provides 16 steps between minimum and maximum values. For finer control, use 5 digits (32 steps, equivalent to the PPM system) or preferably 8 digits (256 steps).

Choosing a method

The choice will nearly always go to the simplest method that provides all the required control features, and works reliably in the given conditions. When choosing a method, any possible expansion of the system in the future should be taken into account.

For any device that is simply to be triggered into action, or switched on for a short period, the single pulse system is the obvious choice. A timing circuit within the controlled device can be used to give longer 'on' periods of fixed duration. If the device is to be switched on for longer periods of variable length and then switched off again, a two-stage sequential system provides the necessary toggle action.

If control of a few functions is required, and there is no objection to switching each on in turn briefly, the next most simple system is the multi-stage sequential system.

✗For larger numbers of functions, and when stepping through them all is not acceptable, the choice lies between a multiple pulse system and PPM. PPM has the advantage that it provides a range of control features, including analogue control by steps. Less effort is required to build the circuits as the coder and decoders are self-contained integrated circuits, requiring the minimum of external wiring. Even if one intends to use only a few of the functions, it may be more economical to base a circuit on these i.c.s rather than attempt to make up coders and decoders from simplest i.c.s.

The error checking features of PPM are important in a noisy environment. However, if the range of functions of the i.c.s does not meet all your requirements, and the environment is not unduly noisy, the 4-digit or 8-digit multiple pulse circuits are a better choice. As explained above, they are particularly suitable for 8-digit analogue control.

For an analogue control system, the choice lies between:

PPM, which is simple to build, has 3 channels, but has only 32 steps, and may be too slow.

Multiple-pulse, more complex to build, only 1 channel, is fast, can have up to 256 steps, giving reliable and precise control.

Digital proportional, fairly easy to build, only 1 channel, infinite number of steps, requires visual or other feed-back, subject to error in noisy environments.

Multiple channels

So far the discussion has assumed that you will have only one controlled device within a given area. If you wish to control two or more devices independently in the same area, you require a multi-channel system. Each device may have its own controller or, where two or more identical devices are to be controlled, there can be one controller which is made to operate each device independently by selecting it with a switch.

There are two ways of making sure that devices are independently controlled. One is to 'tune' the transmission so that only a device tuned to receive it can respond. The other is to restrict the decoders so that they are capable of decoding only a subset of the complete set of signals, and allocate a different subset to each controlled device.

In a radio control system, the transmitter produces a carrier wave that is modulated by the coded signal. The carrier is *completely* modulated, being turned either fully on or fully off (Fig. 4.2). Only a receiver tuned to the same frequency detects and responds to the signal. Several transmitters, each operating on a different frequency can control individual devices in the same area.

The same technique can be applied to other transmission links, such as infra-red, visible light, wire linkage. Instead of

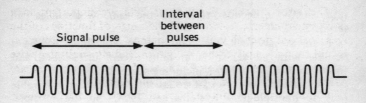

Fig. 4.2 A fully modulated radio carrier wave.

transmitting a series of continuous pulses, the transmitter sends out a series of *tone-bursts*. Their wave-form is shown in Figure 4.3. The carrier frequency is much lower than that of a radio signal. The receiving circuits are tuned to respond only to tone-bursts of a given frequency. The circuitry for producing and detecting tone-bursts are slightly more complicated than those which produce continuous pulses.

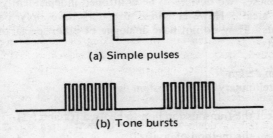

(a) Simple pulses

(b) Tone bursts

Fig. 4.3 (a) Simple pulses. (b) Tone bursts.

In theory, it is possible to apply the tone-burst technique to ultra-sonic control. One could have transmitting and receiving crystals ground to vibrate at various frequencies. In practice only crystals vibrating at 40kHz are readily available, so this technique can not be realized in ultra-sound.

The PPM i.c. has its own tuning system. The basic pulse length of the transmitting i.c. is set by using capacitors and resistors to determine the carrier frequency and modulation

35

rate. Only a decoder tuned to the same frequencies can respond.

From the above it is evident that multi-channel tuning is feasible with all transmission links except ultra-sound and for all methods of control, including analogue control.

The division of a set of codes into sub-sets is applicable only to multiple-pulse systems and PPM. In the multiple-pulse system, the way the sub-sets are determined are under the complete control of the designer. Different devices have identical decoders, but only a given number of the decoder outputs connect to the controlled device. When a signal arrives corresponding to these outputs, action occurs. If the signal corresponds to one of the unconnected outputs, nothing happens. By making the appropriate connections a device can be made to respond to any sub-set of the complete set of signals.

In the PPM system, decoder i.c.s are obtainable which respond only to one of two sub-sets of the control signals. This allows two devices to be controlled independently in the same area. However, these decoders have only program outputs. They do not have analogue or other special purpose outputs.

System design
The preliminary steps of system design are:

1. Select the transmission link to be used (Chapter 2).

2. Select the method of control.

3. If two or more devices are to operate in the same area, decide whether to use 'tuning' or code subsets.

Having done this, look through the chapters that follow to find the circuits that you need.

Chapter 5

THE INPUT INTERFACE

This chapter deals with the various ways in which the commands of the operator may be communicated to the electronic circuits of the remote control system. First it considers the use of buttons and keyboards for all digital systems, followed by a short section on keyboards for PPM. Next, the chapter describes computer interfacing. Finally there is a section on analogue interfaces.

Buttons and keyboards

The most frequently used input device is the push-button. This can either by 'pressed' or 'not pressed', the corresponding command being one of a pair, such as on/off, go/stop, or fast/slow. Care must be taken when deciding what pair of commands are represented by 'pressed' and 'not pressed'. For example, when steering a vehicle, 'pressed' could represent 'turn left' and 'not pressed' could represent 'turn right'. However, under this system, it would be necessary to press and release the button frequently in order to attempt a straight path. The effect would be an undignified zig-zag course! It is better to have two steering buttons, one for left/not-left, one for right/not-right. The not-left and not-right commands both set the steering wheels straight ahead. What happens if *both* buttons are pressed simultaneously? The answer to this question may depend on the nature of the circuitry in the robot, but see later.

The most useful type of push-button is the 'push-to-make' kind. The button is normally open-circuit (contacts separated), and closes the circuit (contacts together) when the button is pressed. Although we refer to a 'button' in the descriptions which follow later, any other kind of make-and-break switch may be used instead.

Closely related to the button is the key-switch. This is the type of switch used in a regular computer keyboard (not the membrane type as used on the Spectrum and many other inexpensive micros). Key switches are usually sold without the key cap. A range of key caps are available separately; some types are plain, but in various colours, others have a detachable transparent cover, so that you may letter or name the keys by inserting a piece of paper or card beneath the cover. Although the smaller type of button is more suitable for a hand-held control panel, key-switches (which are of standard typewriter size) are better for a larger panel. Their size and their light spring-action makes them easier to operate.

It is possible to buy complete keyboard units, ready fitted with a number of key-switches or buttons. These are often expensive but have a neater appearance than many amateurs are able to obtain when fitting individual keys to a panel.

There are other forms of switch that may be applicable to certain types of command. These include:

(a) biassed switch: the switch lever is normally upright; it is pressed to one side to close the switch. The level returns to its upright position and the switch opens immediately pressure is released;

(b) centre-biassed switch: this is really two switches in one unit; the lever is normally upright; it is pressed one way, or the other, to close one switch or the other. The two switches can not be closed at the same time. When pressure is released, the lever returns to its central (upright position) and both switches are open. This is a useful type for 'left-right' and similar controls;

(c) joystick switch: four switches in one, as described on page 8. It is usually centre-biassed;

(d) binary switch: there are several designs, one of the most common having 4 switches in one. These are combined as a rotary switch with 16 positions. As the knob is rotated, the switches are closed in a binary sequence running from all open (0000) to all closed (1111). The output from the switch is the binary equivalent of the decimal values 0 to 15. Other versions may have only 10 positions, giving the sequence 0000 to 1001 (0 to 9).

For a single-pulse or sequential pulse system, a single button, key-switch or biassed switch is sufficient. For a multiple-pulse system or PPM a keyboard made up of a number of buttons, key-switches, biassed switches or centre-biassed switches (or a combination of these types) is generally required. If a binary switch is used with multiple-pulse, it enables rapid selection of up to 10 or 16 functions. The joystick switch is particularly suited to steering applications. Like the centre-biassed switch it obviates the problem referred to above, of what happens if the 'left' and 'right' buttons are pressed at the same time. In addition, pushing a joystick to one side or the other, has a much better 'feel' to it than merely pressing one button or the other.

Circuits for buttons and keyboards

Figures 5.1 and 5.2 show the basic circuits for use with a button. In Figure 5.1 the output terminal is held high by the connection through the *pull-up* resistor R1 to the supply rail.

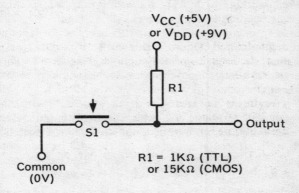

Fig. 5.1 Push–button output which is normally high (1); press for low (0).

Pressing the button (S1) makes a direct connection to the common (ground) rail and the output voltage drops to low. The value of R1 depends on the type of i.c. into which the output is to be fed. The circuit of Figure 5.2 has the opposite

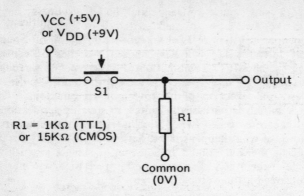

*Fig. 5.2 Push-button output which is normally low (0);
press for high (1).*

action. R1 is referred to as a *pull-down* resistor.

When working with TTL, the connection to V_{CC} through R1 may be omitted from the circuit of Figure 5.1. This is because an unconnected TTL input behaves as if it is connected to a high input. Omitting the link to V_{CC} cuts costs and simplifies the wiring, especially on a large keyboard. On the other hand, CMOS inputs must never be allowed to 'float' in this way.

If a keyboard has several keys, they are each wired up as in Figure 5.1 or Figure 5.2, with a separate output terminal for each switch. Each output terminal of a binary switch also needs to be treated as a separate switch, with its own pull-up or pull-down resistor (Fig. 5.3). Again, the pull-up resistor can be omitted if the switch output is being fed to a TTL input.

Figure 5.4 shows how to wire up a keyboard to give 16 different binary outputs, corresponding to 16 different keys. This is an alternative to the binary switch in multiple-pulse systems. You need wire up only as many keys as you need. The outputs are normally all low, but one or more goes high when a key is pressed.

The problem of key-bounce may cause trouble in sequential-pulse systems. As the switch closes, contact is made and

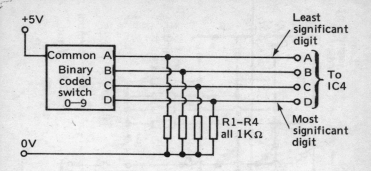

*Fig. 5.3 Connecting a binary coded switch
to the coder of Fig. 6.4*

broken several times before it finally settles into a closed state.
In the sequential system, a single key-press results in a number
of pulses being generated, stepping the controlled device
through an unpredictable number of stages. Figure 5.5a shows
a circuit for de-bouncing a key or button in a TTL system. The
circuit is based on a Schmitt NAND gate with 4 inputs.
Normally all inputs are held high, so the output is low. The
capacitor is charged to the supply voltage. When the key is
pressed, the capacitor gradually discharges and the input
voltage to the NAND gate falls to zero. At a certain voltage,
the *lower threshold voltage*, and below, the input counts as a
low input, and the output of the gate changes sharply from
low to high. If the key contact breaks again, the input voltage
starts to rise, but the gate will not change state again unless
the input voltage rises above the *upper threshold voltage.*
Short-lived breaks are insufficient to raise the input voltage
above the upper threshold, so the gate output remains high.

When the button is released, the input voltage rises, but
there is no change in the state of the gate until the *upper*
threshold is reached. Voltages at this level and above count
as high inputs, so the output of the gate changes sharply to
low at this stage. From then on, a momentary making of
contact is insufficient to make the gate change state again,
since the voltage needs to fall to the lower threshold for this
to happen. In this way the gate shows a sharp rise or fall of

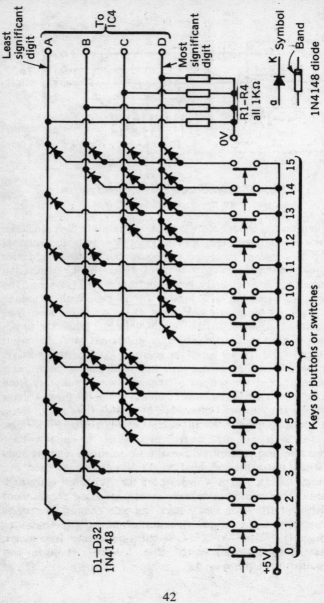

Fig. 5.4 Connecting a keyboard to the coder of Fig. 6.4.

42

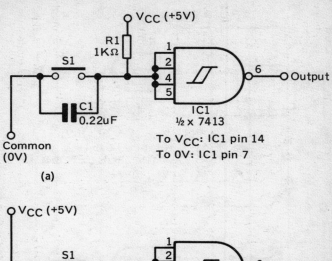

Fig. 5.5 Debouncing keys with TTL:
(a) normally low output; (b) normally high output.

output as the button is pressed or released, and contact bounce is virtually eliminated.

Figure 5.5b shows a debounced key with normally high output. Figure 5.6 shows the two corresponding circuits using CMOS. If there are many keys to be debounced, it is more convenient to use a special contact bounce eliminator i.c., such as the DM8544. This contains 4 separate debouncers, which have the advantage that external resistors and capacitors are not required.

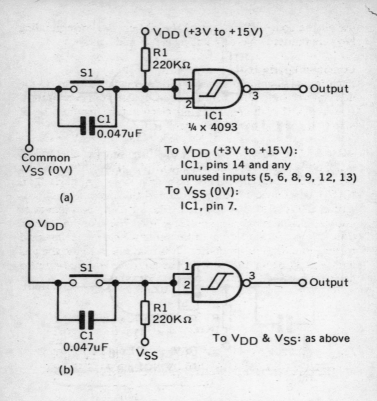

Fig. 5.6 Debouncing keys with CMOS:
(a) normally low output; (b) normally high output.

Keyboards for PPM

These operate on a different principle. The coder i.c. has 8 terminals that are *current sources*, and 3 that are *current sinks*. The keys are wired so that pressing a key connects one of the current sources to one of the current sinks. Depending upon which source is connected to which sink, the appropriate command is registered in the i.c. The wiring of such a keyboard is shown in Figure 6.9. Only 21 of the possible 32 interconnections are valid inputs. If you do not wish to use all the control functions of the system, the corresponding keys are omitted. No debouncing is required.

Computer interfacing

Each model of computer has its own particular features, so the descriptions here refer to the more popular home computers. It is hoped that the explanations given before may also be of help to owners of other computers.

Amstrad CPC 464, 664 and 6128. The simplest method of making the Amstrad computers control a transmitter is to use the output from the printer port (Fig. 5.7). A single TTL NAND i.c. connected to the ground of the computer and data output D0 is all that is required (Fig. 5.8). A short length of double-sided 0.1″ edge-connector is used to make the connection. Note that the 0V rail of the interface *must* be connected to the ground of the computer. It is convenient to use the pad immediately below that of D0. The interface and transmission devices must have their own external 5V supply.

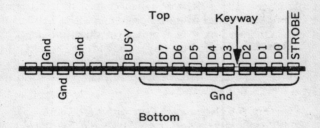

Fig. 5.7. The printer port of the Amstrad, as seen from the rear of the machine.

The state of D0 is controlled by the following BASIC statements:

    10 OUT 61184, 0   — makes D0 go low

    10 OUT 61184, 1   — make D0 go high

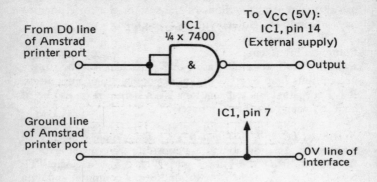

Fig. 5.8. Interfacing to an Amstrad 464, 664 or 6128 computer.

The output of the gate is, of course, the inverse of its input.
The output can be used to drive any of the transmitter devices.
By suitable programming it is possible to make the computer
take the place of the 4-digit or 8-digit coders. It is program-
med to produce a series of pulses beginning with a half-length
start pulse, followed by 4 or 8 pulses. A signal produced by
the computer, transmitted by (say) infra-red, and received by
one of the decoder circuits can be used for controlling a robot
or any similar device. Here we have an example of software
taking the place of hardware.

BBC Microcomputer. The configuration of the User Port is
shown in Figure 5.9. This has a 5V supply which may be used
for powering the interface, provided that it requires only a
few hundred milliamps. For controlling a transmitter we can
use the output from data line 0. The method of connecting a
TTL NAND gate to the BBC Micro is shown in Figure 5.10.
When the machine is first switched on, all lines of the User
Port are inputs. This is to prevent the machine from acci-
dentally operating any attached devices. Before we can use
line D0 as an output, we have to set the Data, Direction
Register for Port B (DDRB) accordingly. The following
program line does this:

46

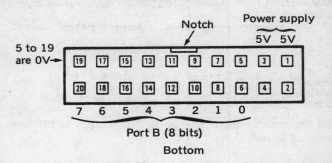

Fig. 5.9 The user port connector of the BBC microcomputer
(model B) as seen from the front,
when the front edge of the machine is lifted.

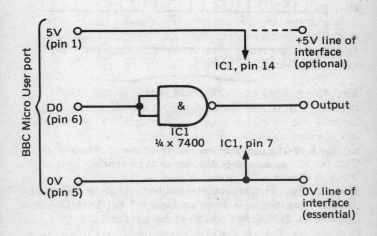

Fig. 5.10 Interfacing to the BBC microcomputer.

10 A%=&97:X%=&62:Y%=1:CALL &FFF4

Next we have to send data to the port:

20 A%=&97:X%=&60:Y%=0:CALL & FFF4

— makes D0 go low

20 A%=&97:X%=&60:Y%=1:CALL & FFF4

— makes D0 go high

See the remarks about how to use the output of D0, in the Amstrad section above.

Commodore 64. The User Port of the 64 (Fig. 5.11) provides 8 data lines that can be used as inputs or outputs. To connect a logic gate to this we use line D0, and the ground connection

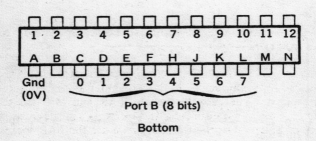

Top (Keyboard side)

Bottom

Fig. 5.11 The user port connector of the Commodore 64, as seen from the rear of the machine.

(Fig. 5.12). The interface must have its own 5V supply. Before using the data lines we must set the Data Direction Register for Port B, so that D0 is in an output:

10 POKE 56579, 1

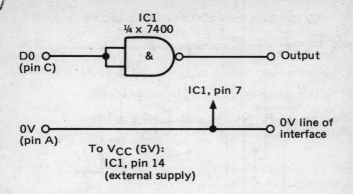

Fig. 5.12 Interfacing to the Commodore 64.

We can now control the level on D0 by using one of the following program lines:

20 POKE 56577,0   — makes D0 go low

20 POKE 56577,1   — makes D0 go high

See the remarks under the Amstrad heading previously on ways to use this output.

Spectrum 48K, + and 128K. The Spectrum does not have a User Port, so interfacing to this computer is slightly more complicated. The cassette sockets, EAR and MIC are the easiest to use for transmitting and receiving a single pulse or series of pulses. For the transmitter we use the EAR socket. The signal from this is not a logic signal (a square wave ranging between 0V and 5V) but a rather 'spikey' signal ranging between −0.8V and +0.8V. The signal is generated by using the BEEP statement. To produce a pulse of suitable duration and pitch, use a statement such as:

10 BEEP 1,48.

Pulse length can be increased or decreased by altering the first parameter. The pitch may be changed by altering the

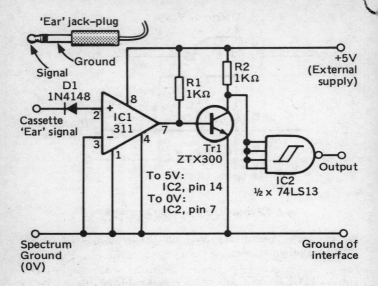

Fig. 5.13 Interfacing to Spectrum computers.

second parameter, but a signal of lower frequency may fail to trigger the circuit. The circuit (Fig. 5.13) first rectifies the signal, by means of D1, so as to produce *negative-going* pulses when the BEEP sounds. A voltage comparator (IC1) detects the signal. Its output voltage, which is normally high, falls slightly. TR1, previously switched on, is now switched off. The input to the NAND Schmitt gate rises and its output goes low. Thus the output from the NAND gate is the inverse of the signal from the Spectrum. This output can be inverted, if required, using the second NAND gate of IC2.

See the remarks under the Amstrad heading previously on ways to use this output.

Analogue interfacing

For speed control, one or more slider resistors or a rotary potentiometer may be used. The general principle of operation is to supply a standard reference voltage across the control resistor, and obtain the output voltage from the wiper

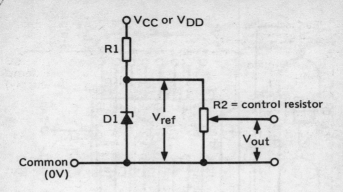

Fig. 5.14 Obtaining a reference voltage.

of the resistor. The reference voltage may be obtained by using a zener diode, as in Figure 5.14. Choose a diode that has a voltage slightly greater than the maximum output voltage required. R1 limits the current through the diode to a level it is designed to carry. If P is the maximum power rating of the diode, and V_z is its zener voltage, then

$$R1 = V_z.V_{CC}/P .$$

It is advisable to use the resistor of next highest value in the standard range.

The output goes to a A-to-D converter or to a proportional pulse generator. In either case the input to these stages must have high impedance, so that current drain from the wiper of the resistor does not cause significant voltage drop at that point. Inputs to converters and pulse generators described in this book meet these requirements.

Low-cost variable resistors use carbon film as the resistive material. Such resistors work satisfactorily when new but, when the track begins to wear, the resistance changes erratically as the wiper is moved. It is preferable to use the more expensive *cermet* resistors, which do not suffer from wear.

A joystick normally has two variable resistors, one for fore-and-aft movement, one for left-and-right. It is preferable for

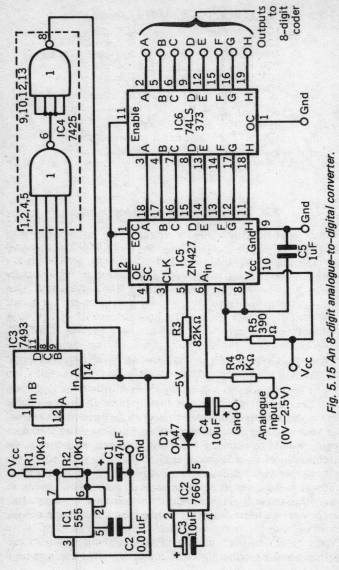

Fig. 5.15 An 8-digit analogue-to-digital converter.

52

To V$_{CC}$ (5V):

ICl, pins 4, 8
IC2, pin 8
IC3, pin 5
IC4, pin 14
IC5, pin 10
IC6, pin 20

To Ground (0V):

IC1, pin 1
IC2, pin 3
IC3, pins 2, 3, 10
IC4, pin 7
IC5, pin 9
IC6, pin 10

Fig. 5.15 (continued) IC power supplies

the joystick to be sprung to return to a central position when
no pressure is applied to the lever.

Circuits for analogue control

The first circuit described (Fig. 5.15) is based on the ZN427
A-to-D i.c. It converts an analogue voltage in the range 0 to
2.5V to an 8-digit output in the range 00000000 (0 decimal)
to 11111111 (255 decimal). The principle on which this i.c.
works is known as *successive approximation*. Conversion
begins when a low pulse is sent to the 'start conversion', pin
(SC). All digits are set to low, except the most significant
(H), which is set to high. The i.c. contains its own D-to-A
converter which, since the digits are now reading 10000000
(128 decimal), produces an output of just over half the
reference voltage. This is compared with the analogue input
voltage. If the average input is greater than the output from
the D-to-A converter, digit H is left as 1, otherwise it is reset
to 0. The same procedure is then applied to the next most
significant digit (G), and so on until all digits have been either
set or reset. The 'end of conversion' (EOC) output then goes
high. While conversion is occurring, outputs from the i.c. are
held low. In our circuit, the EOC pin is connected to the
output enable pin (OE). The high input to this pin causes
outputs to be enabled and the result of conversion appears at
the outputs A to H immediately conversion is completed.

Conversion takes 8 clock periods, with a further period for
enabling the outputs. With a clock running at 1Hz, as in
Figure 5.15 (IC1), conversion takes 9 seconds. The rate can
be increased by reducing the value of C1. The clock is used

to drive the converter directly and also to drive IC3 and IC4 which generate a 'start conversion' pulse every 16 clock periods. Data is present at the output pins for 7 clock periods before the next conversion begins and the outputs are cleared.

The converter needs a −5V line in addition to the usual +5V and ground lines. Since the amount of current required at −5V is small, the supply is provided by a voltage converter i.c. (IC2). With the converter connected as in Figure 5.15, use is made of its interval voltage reference, which is set to 2.5V. The analogue input voltage must not exceed 2.5V. However, an external reference voltage can be used if preferred; for instructions how to do this, consult the manufacturer's data sheets.

The outputs from IC5 are ready for transmission, provided that transmission occurs only when the outputs are enabled. The EOC output can be used to trigger the 8-digit coder described in Chapter 6. In this case IC6 is not required. In other applications it may be preferable for the data to be held on latches until the next conversion has occurred. This means that data is continually present, instead of being cleared while conversion occurs. The figure shows how to use a 74LS373 8-digit latch to hold the data during conversion. At the end of conversion the enable input is made high, and the latest data appears at the outputs of the latches. When EOC goes low at the start of another conversion, the outputs of the latches remain unaffected. They hold the data until the new data appears at the end of the next conversion. Pin 1 of IC6 is the output control pin. This i.c. has 3-state outputs, making it suitable for connecting to a data bus. When OC is made high, the outputs enter a high-impedance state and are effectively disconnected from the bus.

When building the converter, note the polarity of C4; its '+' terminal is connected to the ground rail. If you are including IC6, it is advisable to decouple the positive supply by connecting 0.1μF capacitors between the +5V rail and the ground rail at several points on the circuit board, close to the points at which the ICs draw their supply. Otherwise stray pulses on the supply line can cause the latches to change state unpredictably.

A different and simpler approach to transmitting analogue

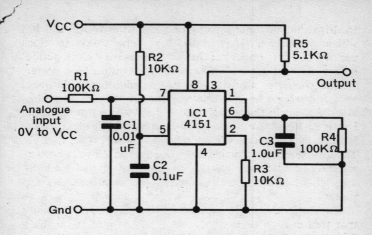

Fig. 5.16 Voltage-to-frequency converter.

data is illustrated by the circuit of Figure 5.16. This is based upon a voltage-to-frequency converter. The circuit accepts an analogue input in the range 0V to V_{CC}. Its output consists of a square wave, the frequency of which is directly proportional to the input voltage. With the values shown in Figure 5.16 the frequency is approximately V_{IN} × 100Hz. The frequency can be increased by increasing the value of R3. The circuit may be operated on any supply voltage in the range 8V to 22V. With 9V supply the current required to drive the circuit is only 5mA, making it suitable for a battery-powered hand-held controller. A circuit of this type has the obvious advantage of simplicity, cheapness, and low power consumption. It is perfectly satisfactory for many purposes. However it has the disadvantage that its accuracy depends upon the relative rates of the clocks in this circuit and the receiving circuit (Fig. 9.6).

If you are intending to use radio as the transmission link, note that the transmitter described on page 97 incorporates two analogue-to-digital converters, making a separate converter unnecessary.

Chapter 6

CODERS

This chapter describes how to build multiple-pulse and PPM coders. These can be used in both digital and analogue systems. If you are designing a single-pulse or sequential pulse system, you will not need to refer to this chapter.

4-digit multiple-pulse coder
Consider a code made up of a train of 4 pulses, of equal length, each of which can be either high (=1) or low (=0). We can make up 16 such trains, arranging the pulses in all possible ways, corresponding to the binary numbers from zero (0000) to 15 (1111). This means that we can transmit up to 16 different instructions by means of this code. For example, we could make up a code for controlling a model aeroplane, and this might have the following form:

Decimal number	Binary number DCBA	Corresponding command
0	0000	No change
1	0001	Centralise control surfaces
2	0010	Move rudder left
3	0011	Move rudder right
4	0100	Move elevators up
5	0101	Move elevators down
6	0110	Move ailerons to roll left
7	0111	Move ailerons to roll right
8	1000	Engine speed 1 (slowest)
9	1001	Engine speed 2
10	1010	Engine speed 3
11	1011	Engine speed 4
12	1100	Engine speed 5
13	1101	Cut engine
14	1110	Landing lights on
15	1111	Landing lights off

If we wish the elevators to move down we transmit the code 0101. Figure 6.1a shows the transmitter output, assuming the digits of the code are transmitted in order D, C, B, A. At the receiver this code is indistinguishable from 1010 (Fig. 6.1b) engine speed 3, so some means of indicating the start of the command message is needed. One way of doing this is to begin *every* command with a high pulse, followed by the four code pulses. Then we have the messages shown in Figures 6.1c and 6.1d; the first or start pulse (S) is half the length of the other pulses because this allows the circuit to be simpler without loss of effectiveness. To follow the operation of the circuit in more detail look at the block diagram (Fig. 6.2).

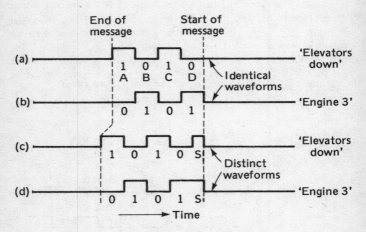

Fig. 6.1 Coded commands.

Pulse length is determined by the clock which produces a continuous series of pulses at approximately 1.5Hz. The system could work just as well with a much higher clock frequency, but the slow clock rate makes it much easier to test the working of the circuit. The clock pulses control the operation of a shift register. This contains a chain of 5 registers, each of which holds data. A 'set' register holds data '1' (output high); a 'reset' register holds data '0' (output low). As the clock output goes from low to high, data is shifted from each register to the next register along the chain. In

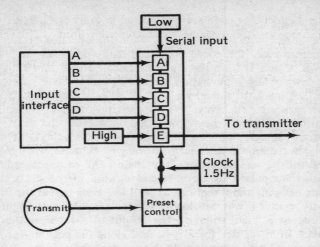

Fig. 6.2 Block diagram of the coder circuit.

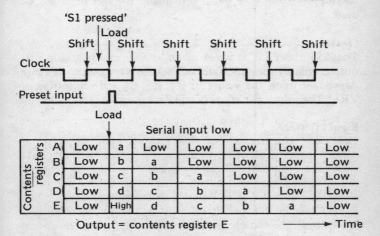

Fig. 6.3 Shifting sequence in the coder.

59

Figure 6.3 we see what happens. To begin with all registers are 'reset', with low outputs. When the operator presses a command key the coded command data appear on the lines A, B, C and D from the input interface. These can be highs or lows in any combination, depending on the code selected, and we represent these by a , b, c, d. These data do not affect the registers yet. Next the operator presses the 'Transmit' button and at the next *low*-going clock pulse the data are loaded directly into the registers (parallel loading). They remain there until the next high-going clock pulse, when they are shifted one step along the chain. At each succeeding high-going pulse they are shifted along until, after 5 shifts, the data has gone and is replaced by all lows. Note that at the first shift register E was 'set' high, because its input is permanently wired to a 'high' voltage. The output of the transmitter is taken from register E. If you read along the bottom line of Figure 6.3 you will find the intended code message: 'start-d-c-b-a', preceded and followed by a continuous 'low' state.

Figure 6.4 shows the circuit details. It operates from a stabilised 5V supply because this is the ideal for the TTL 7400 series i.c.s used. For a portable transmitter you can use a 6V supply (four 1.5V cells) but higher voltages must not be used.

Clock

The 555 timer i.c. is wired as an astable multivibrator. Its output (pin 3) rises and falls as a square-wave output at a rate dependent upon the values of R1, R2, C1 and the setting of VR1. The values give *roughly* equal mark-space ratio.

Input interface

The exact construction of this depends upon the type of control panel preferred. It is simplest to use a switch that gives binary output. These are available as slide switches or thumbwheel rotary switches that can be set to any one of 10 positions. If wired as in Figure 5.3, the voltage on each line is held low by the pull-down resistor, except when connected through the switch to the positive supply. As the switch is rotated or slid from position 0 to position 9, the lines

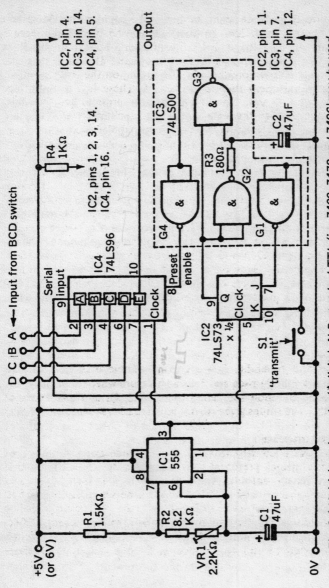

Fig. 6.4 Multiple-pulse coder (4 digits). N.B. standard TTL (i.e. 7400, 7473 and 7496) may be used.

61

carry voltages equivalent to binary numbers from 0000 to 1001. This allows you to work with up to 10 different commands. If you need more, or if you prefer to use press-buttons, toggle-switches or keys, construct a diode matrix as in Figure 5.4 to produce the outputs you require. You may need all 16 but, if you do not, you may find that it simplifies decoding problems later if you choose carefully which codes are to correspond with a given set of commands. For example, if all engine-speed codes have digit D high, this makes it easier at a later stage to pick out engine-speed commands from commands of other types.

If you use a binary coded switch, this retains its output until you change the setting of the switch at the next command. If you are using press-buttons or keys, these must be held depressed for long enough *after* the 'Transmit' button has been pressed to allow time for the command to be registered. With the given clock speed, this period is a minimum of about 0.6 second.

Shift register

For this we use a 74LS96 i.c. The low power Schottky TTL is preferred because its low power requirements make it more suitable for battery operation. If you are planning to power your equipment from a mains power-pack, there is no reason why the slightly cheaper standard TTL i.c., the 7496, should not be used. The same applies to the other TTL i.c.s of this circuit. The serial input is wired to common permanently, to reset register A at each shift. The input of register E is wired to V_{cc} (5V or 6V) so that this is set every time the preset enable is pulsed, that is, when a train of pulses is about to be transmitted. The outputs from registers A to D are not used. The clear input (pin 16) is not used, but must be connected to V_{cc} through a 1kΩ resistor, which it can share with unused inputs of other i.c.s that must similarly be held high.

Preset control

The purpose of this is to generate a brief high pulse on the first low-going clock pulse following the pressing of 'Transmit' button, S1. This must happen once and once only, and no further pulse is allowable during the process of shifting the

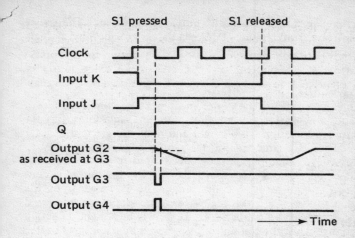

Fig. 6.5 Voltage levels in the coder circuit.

data out of the register. Figure 6.5 explains the working of this part of the circuit. When S1 is pressed, the K input to the flip-flop (half of IC2) goes low and the input to J (via inverting gate G1) goes high. With the inputs to the flip-flop in this condition the output of the flip-flop (Q) goes high at the next *low*-going clock pulse. It will remain high until the next low-going clock pulse after the button is released. As Q goes high, so does one input to G3. The input to G2 goes high and its output falls but, because of R3 and C2, the other input to G3 does not fall quite as quickly. For a brief period both inputs to G3 are effectively high, and its output goes low.

The effect is quickly over and, as the delayed fall to low input takes effect, G3 has one input high and the other low, so its output becomes high again. Thus a brief low pulse is obtained from G3; this is inverted by G4, giving a brief high pulse that enables the transfer of data from the input interface to the registers. After this stage, S1 may be released; Q goes low and, though the output from G2 to G3 rises slowly, the fact that the other input to the gate (fed by Q) is already low means that no low output is obtained from G3. Once the preset enable pulse has been produced, the data is shifted to the transmitter under the control of clock, and it makes no

63

difference if the 'Transmit' button is released. The preset control circuit requires 4 NAND gates, provided by a single 74LS00 (or 7400) i.c.

Transmitter

The output from the coder must next be converted into a form suitable for transmission. Methods of doing this for infra-red radiation, visible light and radio are given in Chapter 7. The ultra-sonic transmitter can be connected directly to this coder. Simply join the coder output to pin 1 of the i.c. There is no need to remove R1 of the transmitter circuit. Both transmitter and coder should be powered from the same source — a 5-volt regulated mains supply, or (preferred for portability) a 6V battery. There will be a slight reduction in range when the transmitter is powered by 6V instead of 9V, but this has been found to be negligible. On no account must the coder be operated from the 9V supply as this will over-run the TTL i.c.s. With the coder so connected ultra-sound is produced continuously and goes *off* when a high pulse is generated from the coder. In other words, the signal transmitted is the *inverse* of the signal produced by the coder. This is of no consequence, provided it is remembered and the decoding circuit in the receiver designed accordingly.

If it is essential for the transmitter to produce the code exactly as it comes from the coder, the coder output must be inverted before it is fed to the transmitter. This is simply done by using a transistor, connected as in Figure 6.6. Here the 15kΩ resistor is an essential part and must not be removed from the circuit. S1 of the transmitter can be retained to allow pulses to be sent manually for other applications.

Analogue control

This coder can also be used for low-resolution analogue coding. Four outputs are taken from the A-to-D converter. These can be the least significant four, the most significant four, or perhaps four alternate outputs. This gives only 16 steps on the analogue scale. If higher resolution is required, use the 8-digit coder described in the next section.

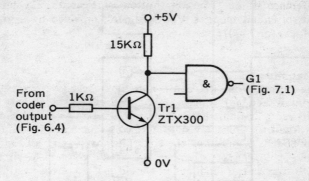

Fig. 6.6 Inverting the output of the coder.

8-digit multiple pulse coder

The block diagram of the 8-digit coder is shown in Figure 6.7. This produces 256 different codes, which is considerably more than the reader is likely to need for digital control purposes. Its main purpose is for analogue control, since it can code all 8 digits from an A-to-D converter. Another difference between this coder and the 4-digit coder is that this one operates continuously, coding the latest value of the digital input and transmitting it automatically. This is done so that the controlled device obeys the changes in joystick (or slider resistor) position as they occur. Continuous coding is not appropriate to input from a binary switch, because it runs through all intermediate values while being switched from one value to another. This is why the 4-digit coder has a 'transmit' key.

The circuit (Fig. 6.8) has many features in common with that of the 4-digit coder (Fig. 6.4). There is an additional shift register to accommodate the extra 4 digits. Instead of the 'transmit' button, there is a divide-by-32 counter. This produces a 'preset' pulse every 32 pulses. This is the equivalent to the operator pressing the 'transmit' button regularly every 21 seconds.

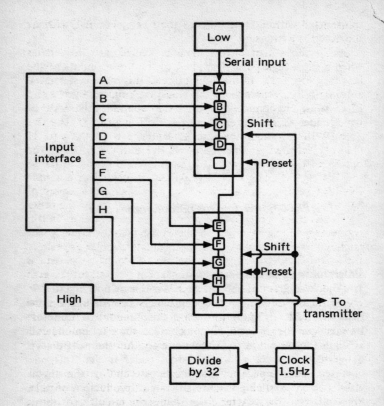

Fig. 6.7 Block diagram of the 8-digit coder circuit.

If you have already built the 4-digit version it is easy to convert it to the 8-digit version. There is a second 5-digit shift register, IC5, connected in series with the first shift register. The data from the fourth latch (D) of the first register is fed to the serial input of the second register. Thus the data is shifted along a chain of 9 latches, A to I, with I providing the half-length 'start' pulse. Note that the fifth register of IC4 is unused. The 8-bit coder can be used with a keyboard such as that of Figure 5.4, using inputs A to D. The inputs corresponding to digits E to H are wired to 0V. Commands are

66

transmitted within 21 seconds of their being entered, without the need for a 'transmit' key.

As in the 4-digit circuit, data is loaded into the latches when a short high pulse is applied to the preset inputs of the i.c.s (see Fig. 6.3). In the 8-digit circuit this pulse is generated automatically. Pulses from the clock are counted by IC2 and IC6. These are connected as a 32-step counter, the output of which changes state every time the clock goes low. The five outputs run through the binary sequence 0 (00000) to 31 (11111) repeatedly. Every time all five outputs are high, the output of the NAND gate (IC7) goes low. Thus the output at the first NAND gate of IC3 which is connected as a simple INVERT gate, is normally low, but goes high on the count of 31. This triggers the pulse generator made up by the other 3 gates of IC3 (as Fig. 6.4) to produce the preset pulse. In this way, the data being input to the coder is transferred to the latches every 31st count, and the high 'start' pulse appears at the output of latch I. For the next 8 counts, the data is shifted along the registers and appears at the output of latch I. When this has finished, all latches will have been set to low, owing to the low input being continually present at the serial input of IC4. The output from the circuit will therefore remain low for the next 22 counts. On the 21st count, data is again transferred to the latches and another train of pulses is generated.

For certain applications, especially the coding of analogue data such as joystick positions, the rate of production of pulse trains is too slow. After constructing the circuit and testing it, substitute a $4.7\mu F$ capacitor for C1. This will speed up the operation of the circuit tenfold, transmitting fresh data every 2 seconds. For faster transmission, use a capacitor of even lower value for C1.

A simplification of the circuit is possible if it is used in conjunction with the A-to-D converter of Figure 5.15. The EOC (end of conversion) output is connected to the preset inputs of the coder circuit of Figure 6.8. As soon as a conversion is complete, the shift registers are loaded with the latest data and the pulse train is generated. The EOC pulse takes the place of the 'preset' pulse from IC3 of Figure 6.8. ICs 2, 3, 6 and 7 of Figure 6.8 are not then required. The rate of

67

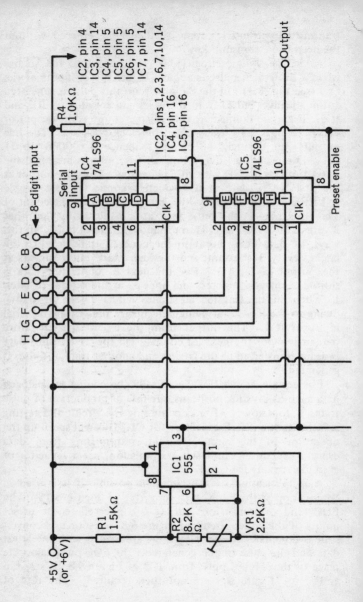

68

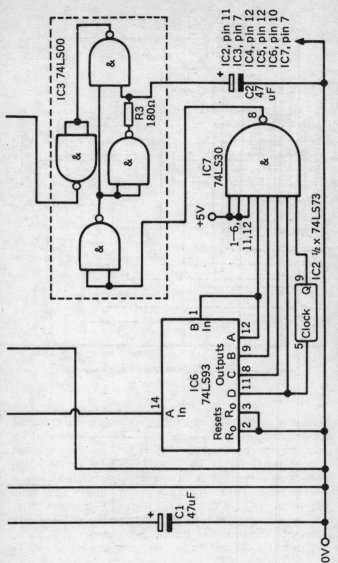

Fig. 6.8 8-digit multiple-pulse coder.

69

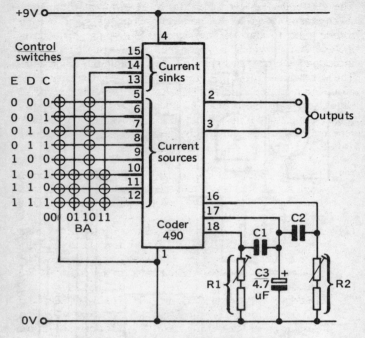

Fig. 6.9 Basic circuit for the PPM coder IC.

conversion must be adjusted so that it takes at least twice the time taken to transmit the pulse train. This is to prevent the decoder picking up successive trains half-way through and misinterpreting them. If the clock of the coder runs at 1.5Hz, it takes 8 periods to shift the train and requires at least a further 8 periods between trains. For safety, conversion should occur every 20 periods, every 13 seconds. This represents 9 clock periods of the converter clock (Fig. 5.15). The clock of the converter should therefore run at 0.7Hz or less. This rate could be obtained by increasing R1 and R2 to 15k.

PPM coder

The 490 coder i.c. can accept up to 21 different commands. A command is given by connecting one of eight *current source* pins to one of four *current sink* pins. The latter include pin 1 which is grounded. Only the connections indicated by circles in Figure 6.9 give meaningful commands. The commands may be thought of as 5-digit binary code groups, having the format EDCBA. Figure 6.9 is marked to show how each group may be coded by striking the appropriate key. There is no need to fit more keys than are actually required to give the commands you need. The commands are as follows:

(1) *Program codes* (0000X to 1001X): In these 10 codes, digit A is ignored by the coder. The four digits E to B can thus be thought of as a 4-digit binary number, coding programs 0 to 9.

(2) *Program step* (10101, 11101): These cause the program outputs of the decoder i.c. to step through their sequence 0 to 9 forward or backward, respectively. The rate of stepping is controlled by a timing circuit at the decoder.

(3) *Analogue increase* (10100, 10110, 10111): The decoder i.c. has 3 outputs, 'Analogue 1', 'Analogue 2', and 'Analogue 3'. These are useful for the control of motor speeds and other analogue functions. These are not true analogue outputs, for they increase by steps, but since there are 32 steps in the range of each output the degree of control is sufficiently fine for most purposes. Pressing and holding an analogue increase key causes the analogue output to be stepped up at a predetermined rate until it reaches its maximum value, after which there is no further increase. The outputs come from *current* regulators; a reference current can be set at the decoder i.c. and this determines the level of currents supplied from the analogue outputs.

(4) *Analogue decrease* (11100, 11110, 11111): These commands make the analogue outputs step down, continuing until zero current output is reached.

(5) *Standby* (11000): This controls the 'On/Standby'

output of the decoder i.c. When the i.c. is first switched on, this output is high. When a program code or program step command is received, it goes low. It goes high again when a standby command is received.

(6) *Toggle output* (11001): Controls the 'toggle' output on the decoder i.c. This is initially low, but changes to high when Analogue 2 output is brought to zero level.

(7) *Normalise* (11011): At this command, all analogue outputs are taken to 12/8 of reference current, and the 'toggle' output is taken to low.

From the description above it is clear that the range of control functions that may be achieved by this pair of i.c.s is enormous and limited principally by the imagination and ingenuity of the user. In planning a particular project, it becomes a fascinating exercise to make the very best of the facilities offered.

Frequency setting

If transmission is to be by ultra-sound, or by tone bursts of visible light or infra-red, or if a modulated signal is to be sent by cable, a *carrier frequency* must be generated. The circuits for doing this are contained within the coder i.c. and require only a timing capacitor C1 and resistor R1. Figure 6.9 shows that R1 should consist of a fixed resistor plus a variable preset resistor so that the frequency may be set to the desired value. The equation for calculating frequency is:

$$f \approx \frac{1}{C_1 R_1}$$

where f is in hertz, C_1 in farads and R_1 in ohms. The resistor should have a value between 20kΩ and 80kΩ, and f may take any value up to and including 200kHz. If no carrier frequency is required, as in *un*modulated infra-red transmission, omit C1 and wire a fixed resistor, value 2.2kΩ for R1.

The other frequency that must be set is the *modulation rate*. This determines t_0, the time for a '0' interval. The '1' interval then has 2/3 of this value, and the 'S' interval is twice the '0'

72

interval.   The equation for calculating modulation rate is:

$$t_0 \approx 1.4C_2R_2$$

where t_0 is in seconds, C_2 is in farads, and R_2 is in ohms. The resistor should have a value between $15k\Omega$ and $100k\Omega$, and t_0 can lie between 1s and 0.1ms.

Choice of carrier frequency depends upon the mode of transmission.   For most ultra-sonic crystals, the resonant frequency is approximately 40kHz and the values of C1 and R1 must be chosen so as to obtain this. Choice of modulation rate is affected mainly by the length of time required for the stepping of the analogue outputs through their full range. Although the time required to transmit and receive a command may be a matter of only a few hundred millisecond, the analogue outputs have 32 steps and the stepping command must be transmitted and received for each of these steps. In practice each command must be transmitted and received *twice* before it is effected, since the decoder has an error-checking feature that requires it to receive the same code twice in succession before it responds. This means that the time taken to step from one end of the scale to the other may exceed 10s even when t_0 is only 27ms, a bit rate of 37/s. If an ultra-sonic transmitter is being used it is not possible to decrease t_0 to less than 13ms without some loss of range, for the transducer rise-time is of the order of 2ms. Using infra-red and radio, t_0 may be as little as the minimum, 0.1s.

Outputs

When a key is pressed the corresponding 5-bit code is transmitted, followed by the synchronising 'S' bit, and this sequence is repeated for as long as the key is held down. When the key is released the coder continues to the end of a code group and then stops. There are two output pins, each producing pulses in antiphase (Fig. 6.10), modulated or not, depending on whether C1 is included in the circuit.

A further output is available from pin 17. This is normally low, but goes high whenever a key is pressed. This output is useful, for it can operate an LED to give indication that a signal is being transmitted. Excessive current drain must be

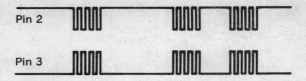

Fig. 6.10 Output waveforms.

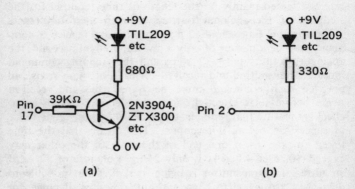

Fig. 6.11 Providing visual indication of transmission.

avoided, so this indicator must be driven by a transistor, as shown in Figure 6.11a. A simpler method of indicating transmitting action may be employed if output 2 is not required for activating the transducer. As Figure 6.10 shows, the output of pin 2 is high when pulses are *not* being transmitted. An LED wired as in Figure 6.11b is dark between pulses but flashes when a code group is being transmitted.

The way the outputs are used for transmission depends on the kind of transducer involved. For ultra-sonic control the transducer may be connected directly to pins 2 and 3. These provide a current up to 5mA which is sufficient to give the transmitter a range of up to 8m. For greater range, up to 10m, extra power may be gained by using outputs 2 and 3 to drive

74

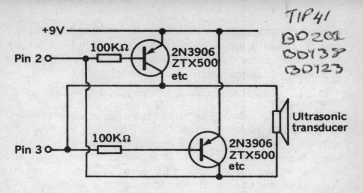

Fig. 6.12 Increasing the range of an ultrasonic transmitter.

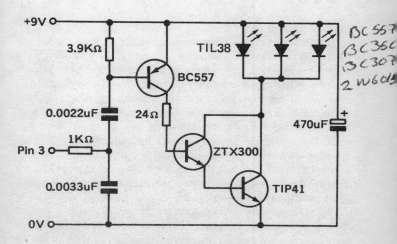

Fig. 6.13 Driving infra-red LEDs.

transistors, as in Figure 6.12 so as to pull the voltage on one line almost to +9V when the voltage on the other line is zero.

The current available from pins 2 and 3 is insufficient to drive a high-power infra-red LED, so this (or *these* if greater range is required) must be driven by transistors. A circuit is given in Figure 6.13 for high power LED transmission. This uses pin 3, which has low output between pulses, leaving pin 2 free to power a visible light LED as indicator (Fig. 6.11b). This circuit can be used either with modulated transmission or unmodulated transmission.

Power supply

Whereas many other systems of transmission require several i.c.s, resulting in heavy current drain, the 490 requires only $6\mu A$ while on standby. While transmitting, the power requirement depends on the mode of transmission employed and whether or not an indicator LED is included in the circuit. For ultra-sonic transmission or when using a single infra-red LED, sufficient power can be supplied by a PP3 battery. This is very convenient if a small hand-held transmitting unit is to be built.

Control panel

In the PPM system all commands are made by pressing keys or operating switches. There is no convenient way in which the joystick control lever of the digital proportional system with its two potentiometers can be coupled to the system. The function of the joystick or steering-wheel control is taken over by pairs of keys. One advantage is the reduction in cost; another is the long-lasting nature of key contacts compared with the tendency to wear shown by potentiometer tracks. Users of joysticks may at first find the unfamiliarity of key-control a drawback, but one soon becomes accustomed to the new method. As an alternative to a pair of keys for operations such as 'left—right', 'forward—backward' or 'climb—dive', a single-pole changeover toggle switch, with a central 'off' position may be used. These switches can be mounted on the control panel, orientated so that the direction of movement of the switch lever corresponds with directional commands. If desired, a piece of plastic or metal tubing can be attached to the lever to lengthen it, so that it almost resembles a joystick in action and appearance. Again there is a considerable saving in cost.

For digital functions, such as Program Control, Program Step, Normalise etc., simple keyboard switches can be used. Before laying out the keyboard give thought to the frequency with which certain keys will need to be operated, and their

sequence of operation, so that the keyboard will be convenient to handle. Apart from the keys, the only other item on
the control panel is the indicator LED and, possibly another
LED connected so as to indicate that power is switched on.

Dual control

The coder operates at a preset modulation rate and, as will be
described later, the decoder i.c. responds only to signals that
have the correct modulation rate. It is therefore a simple
matter to operate two or more pairs of transmitters and
receivers in the same area without any danger of interference.
The only concern is to set the modulation rates so that they
are different by a sufficient factor. Similarly, a single coder
i.c. can be wired as in Figure 6.14 so that its modulation rate
can be switched to one of two (or more) values. Two (or
more) decoders can then be tuned each to respond to a different frequency, giving independent control of two devices
from a single transmitter.

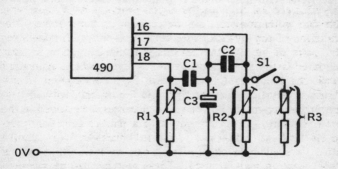

*Fig. 6.14 Switching resistor chains in parallel
to give two different modulation rates.*

Tuning the coder and decoder

Ideally this should be done with the help of an oscilloscope.
The output from the coder i.c. is monitored so that the length
of t_0 can be adjusted to the required value. If the transmitter
is to be used with an ultra-sonic crystal transducer, the carrier
frequency is also monitored and adjusted to 40kHz, or whatever the resonant frequency of the crystal may be. The

transmitter and receiver are then placed a few metres apart and a transmitter key held down, so as to transmit any one of the program signals 1—9 continuously. The receiver circuit may then be adjusted for maximum response. It may also be necessary to readjust carrier frequency in the transmitter to obtain maximum response in the receiver. The oscillator frequency (pin 6) Figure 9.4 should also be monitored and adjusted until its period is 1/40th of that of t_0.

Those without an oscilloscope may find that it takes a little more time and trouble to obtain good transmission and reception but the task is not too difficult. One has to rely on the component values at the transmitter being within a small tolerance range, otherwise it may not be possible to adjust oscillator frequency to 1/40th of t_0. The use of close-tolerance components for R2 and C2 in the transmitter and for C1 and R2 in the receiver will help reduce the element of uncertainty. With the transmitter in continuous operation *slowly* adjust VR1 (Fig. 9.4) until a response is obtained at the receiver. Remember that a response may take a second or two to appear if reception is bad.

Chapter 7

TRANSMISSION

Advice on choosing which type of transmission link to use is given in Chapter 2. This chapter describes practical ways of putting your choice into effect. The final section in this chapter explains how to implement multi-channel systems by using the tone-burst technique (see also the last section of Chapter 4).

Ultra-sound

The circuit in Figure 7.1 is a complete ultra-sonic transmitter for single-pulse control. It is an easy project for the beginner. The corresponding receiver is described in Chapter 8.

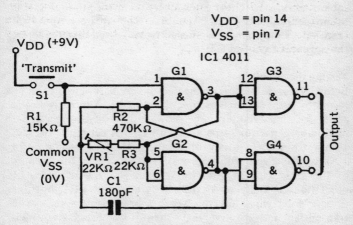

Fig. 7.1 Simple ultra-sonic transmitter oscillator.

The transducer (or transmitter, as it is sometimes called) consists of a crystal specially ground so as to resonate vigorously when a 40kHz signal is applied across its terminals.

The oscillator circuit is built from four NAND logic gates and, since the CMOS 4011 i.c. contains four such gates, we need only one i.c. and a few external components. These can all be accommodated on a very small piece of 0.1 inch matrix stripboard. Only a small battery is needed (a PP3), so the whole transmitter can be contained in a small case, making it ideal for a hand-held control.

The heart of the circuit is the astable multivibrator, consisting of two gates (G1, G2) and their associated components. The multivibrator alternates between two states. In one state the output of G1 is high (+9V) and that of G2 is low (0V). In the other state the output of G1 is low and that of G2 is high. The multivibrator changes state at a rate dependent upon the values of R3, VR1 and C1. With the values given in Figure 7.1 change of state occurs 40,000 times a second, giving the 40kHz output required for making the transducer crystal resonate.

The outputs from the multivibrator are not perfectly square waves, so they are fed to a second pair of gates (G3, G4) to square them off. These gates invert them too, though this is of no consequence in this circuit. The square outputs are then fed to the transducer, which is connected directly across the outputs of G3 and G4.

Testing the circuit
Before the transducer is connected the oscillator circuit can be tested by using an oscilloscope, if available. Alternatively the action of the circuit can be slowed down by connecting a high-value capacitor in parallel with C1. A capacitor of, say, $100\mu F$, gives a frequency of about 0.1Hz (one oscillation in 10 seconds) giving you plenty of time to check the outputs of the gates with an ordinary voltmeter. The frequency of oscillation is finally set to 40kHz by adjusting VR1, but this is best done when the receiver has been constructed. The transmitter and receiver may then be adjusted to obtain maximum operating range.

Using the transmitter
This circuit has no coder so only on—off or stop—go commands may be transmitted. This is sufficient for many applications, such as stopping or starting an electric train, or switching a radio set on and off. In Chapter 10 there are circuits that improve upon this by allowing the controlled

device to step through a sequence of different operatic...
time a pulse is received. In other applications a coded s...
pulses may be required and for this purpose a coder may b...
connected to this transmitter circuit (Chapter 6).

Infra-red

A very simple transmitter for single-pulse operation is shown
in Figure 7.2. The TIL38 LED is a large and powerful emitter

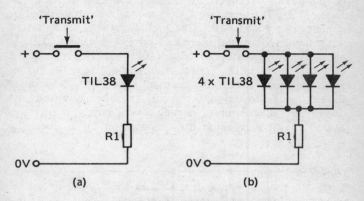

Fig. 7.2 Infra-red transmitters.

of infra-red radiation. Its maximum current consumption is
150mA, so the resistor must be chosen to give a current close
to that value if maximum range is to be attained. For 5V
operation the resistor should be 22Ω, and for 10V operation
it should be 56Ω. A single LED without any form of reflector
or lens to focus a beam has a range of up to 1 metre. To
increase the range one simply adds more LEDs in parallel, as
in Figure 7.2b. For 5V operation, the resistor should have
the value 5.6Ω, for 10V it should be 15Ω. Three or four such
LEDs should be sufficient for control purposes when used in
an ordinary living-room or office.

A transmitter of the kind described above can also be
driven by a multi-pulse coder and from a PPM coder as described in Chapter 6.

Although the maximum continuous current for the TIL38 is large compared with that of many other types of LED, it can be increased even further provided that this is done for very short periods. If pulses are limited in length to 10μs, and transmitted no more often than once per millisecond, the current through the LED may be as much as 2A, giving a very intense flash of radiation. This is another way of increasing range, though the circuit required is more complex and the use of several LEDs in parallel as in Figure 7.2b is generally to be preferred. A circuit for flashing the LED is shown in Figure 7.3. This uses two CMOS monostable multivibrators, contained in a single i.c. One multivibrator is set to give a 'long flash' (about half a second) on a visible light LED, as an indication that the short flash (10μs) has been transmitted by the infra-red LED. Transmission takes place as the button is first pressed. Though the use of a simple button is adequate for setting-up and testing the circuit, trouble may arise in use owing to contact-bounce, causing several pulses to be transmitted. This *may* cause little trouble but, if it does, the

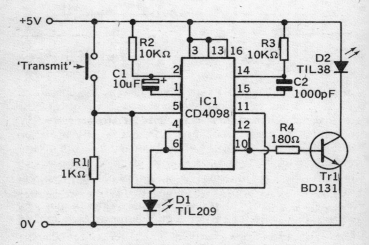

Fig. 7.3 An infra-red pulse transmitter for short high-intensity pulses.

82

triggering of the monostables should be done by a logic input, such as obtainable from a Schmitt trigger gate (page 43), or from the output of one of the coding circuits described elsewhere in this book.

One final point concerning transmitters is that the *miniature* infra-red LEDs (e.g. TIL32) are unsuitable for this application because of their low emission. They are intended only for close-range detection, such as in punched-tape reading.

Visible light

Figure 7.4 shows the main features of a visible light transmission link. A link can also be made by using optical fibre (see later). For single-pulse and sequential pulse system, the minimum requirement is a switch or button to turn the lamp on and off. However, as mentioned in Chapter 2, a visible light link is particularly subject to interference from other sources of illumination, including daylight. This interference can be minimised by using tone-burst transmission or an optical fibre link, as explained later in this chapter.

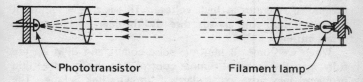

Phototransistor   Filament lamp

Fig. 7.4 Transmission by focussed visible light beam.

The multiple-pulse coder (Chapter 6) can be readily adapted to operate a small filament lamp. The output from the circuit of Figure 6.4 is taken directly to the transmitter circuit of Figure 7.5. The pair of transistors provides gain sufficient to power the lamp which, being slightly over-run, gives a strong signal that will carry for a considerable distance, even without excessively careful alignment of the beam.

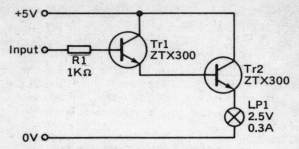

Fig. 7.5 Visible light transmitter interface.

Wired link

Perhaps an electric door-bell is the most common and elementary form of remote control possible. The input interface is linked directly to the controlled device by a pair of wires. It might be considered that such a circuit hardly ranks as remote control! But a slight variation on this, in which a push-button remotely activates a relay, which in turn switches on a mains-powered electric motor has several features of a fully-fledged remote control system. The signal is sent at low voltage, yet the motor operates at high voltage. This is a safer approach than switching the motor directly through wires carrying mains currents.

When we come to multiple-pulse coders and PPM we are fully into the realm of remote control. At this point certain problems may arise, particularly if the wire link is long. The output terminals of TTL and other i.c.s are not normally designed for passing signals into long wires. The wires have high impedance to high-frequency signals, with their rapidly changing voltage levels. This leads to distortion of the signals, which may fail to reach the other end of the wire. In addition, the longer the line the greater the amount of noise picked up along the way, making the signal difficult to recognise at the receiving end. We describe both the driver and the receiver circuits in this chapter, since they are electrically connected.

In order to overcome problems with long and noisy lines we need outputs that are capable of delivering a greater current at high frequencies. Such *line-driver* circuits are available as i.c.s. Figures 7.6 to 7.9 show how to use line-drivers when passing the output of a multiple-pulse coder, PPM coder or voltage-to-frequency converter into a wire link.

When you first set up a wired system, try simply connecting the transmitter and receiver together by a twisted pair of wires. The twisting helps minimize interference and, provided the wire is not too long, there may be no need for a special line-driver and receiver. If this proves to be unsatisfactory, then the next simplest technique is direct TTL drive, as illustrated in Figure 7.6. Any TTL gate can be used as an output, except that outputs from flip-flops, shift-registers and similar devices should not be used. Receiving is best done by a Schmitt trigger gate, such as the INVERT gate shown.

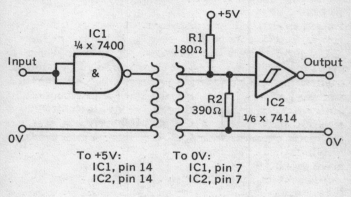

Fig. 7.6 Direct TTL line driver and receiver.

The input terminal of this gate is held in between the threshold points by the two resistors. Thus it is ready to respond to any upward or downward change in input voltage. The Schmitt gate produces a sharp square-wave output which may then be fed to TTL or CMOS circuits. If noise is a problem, a resistor-capacitor filter may be added (R3 and C1) as shown in Figure 7.7.

Figure 7.8 shows a variation on the above technique using two specialized i.c.s. Voltages obtained are compatible with RS-232C serial interfaces. IC1 contains 4 line-drivers, 3 of

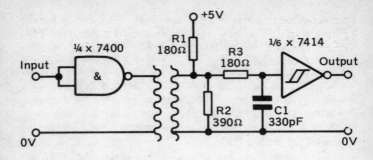

Fig. 7.7 Direct TTL line driver and receiver
for noisy conditions.

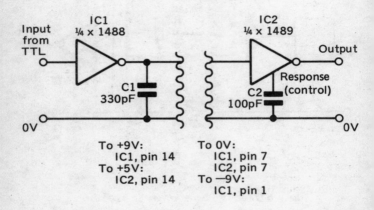

Fig. 7.8 RS–232C line driver and receiver.

which are 2-input NAND gates and 1 of which is an INVERT gate. Each gate requires input from a TTL gate, the input levels being 0V (approximately) for low and 5V (approximately) for high. The corresponding outputs from the gate are +7V and −7V, when run on a ±9V supply. The i.c. requires only a small current at −9V, so can be powered from a 9V battery with a 7660 voltage converter i.c. (see Fig. 5.15, IC2, D1 and C3). At the other end of the line there is the corresponding line receiver i.c., the 1489. This can be power-ed by a single 5V supply, to provide output suitable for TTL. The i.c. contains 4 receiver gates, each of which has a control input. A capacitor connected to this input helps reduce the effects of noise on the line.

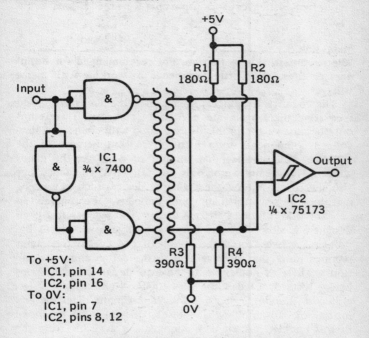

Fig. 7.9 Differential TTL line driver and receiver.

For long transmission lines, use a differential TTL drive, as in Figure 7.9. Instead of one line being a ground line, one line transmits the signal and the other the inverted signal. This may be done by using a differential line driver (such as the 75172) or more cheaply by using the TTL NAND or INVERT gates. The 75173 produces a normal TTL output.

The cost of the cable is a major consideration in a wired link. If the system later needs to be expanded, the cost of laying new cable increases the overall cost of the system still further. The use of multiple-channel techniques, such as the dividing of code signals into subsets, or the tone-burst technique, described at the end of this chapter, makes it possible for several transmission links to share the same pair of wires. This can prove most economic, and makes a limited amount of system expansion possible for no additional cable cost.

Mains link
The circuits in this section are not recommended for beginners or those with little experience of working with mains voltages.

The circuitry for putting signals on to the mains wiring and recovering them again are necessarily complex. This is not only because of the problems associated with connecting low-voltage components to a high-voltage, but because of the presence of a considerable amount of noise on the mains wires. This includes not only the 50Hz AC frequency but also the spikes put on the mains by devices such as washing machines, refrigerators, and lamp-dimmers. Fortunately an i.c., the LM Bi-line Carrier Current Transceiver, has been designed specially for the purpose, and greatly reduces the problems. Even so, the coupling of the i.c. to the mains requires more than average skill in the design and construction. There is not space to go into design considerations here. Instead, we describe how to use a unit which is described in *Maplin Projects, Book 16*. Circuit diagrams and instructions for building and testing the units are described in this booklet. A kit of components is available from the supplier listed in Appendix C.

The device plugs into any ordinary mains socket and will then be able to communicate with a second device of the same kind plugged into any other mains socket in the house. It is able to transmit digital data or receive it, but not both at the same time. The connections to be made to the device are by means of a 6-way plug on the board, as shown in Figure 7.10. All of these terminals are wired only to opto-couplers so there is no electrical connection between these and any part of the unit's circuit. Data inputs can be from TTL i.c.s or from RS-232 i.c.s, such as the line-driver of Figure 7:8.

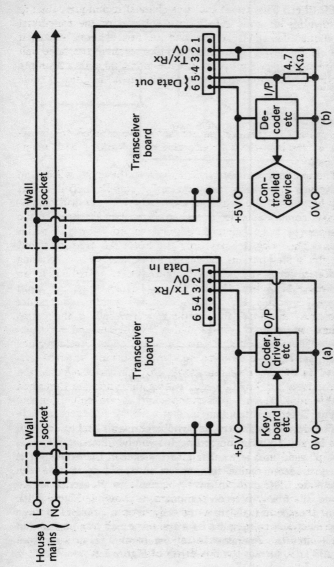

Fig. 7.10 Connecting the mains transceiver as (a) a transmitter; (b) a receiver

89

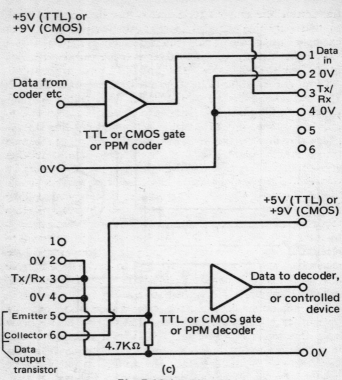

Fig. 7.10 (continued)
(c) connecting CMOS and TTL gates to the transceiver.

The device contains an oscillator which produces a high-frequency (125kHz) carrier signal. This is shifted to 127.750 kHz or 122.500kHz, according to whether the data input is low or high, and transmitted to the mains. The receiver is tuned to detect these frequencies and produce low or high output accordingly. If several devices are plugged into the mains, all those in 'receive' mode will respond to the signal from a single transmitter. In theory, it is possible to tune each receiver to respond to a different set of frequencies, but this makes the operation of a system unnecessarily complicated. If you wish to control several receivers from one transmitter, the simplest technique is to code the signal itself, so that only the intended receiver can respond to it. For example, using the 4-digit multiple-pulse system the first two digits identify which receiver is being called. Thus all four of codes 0000, 0001, 0010 and 0011 refer to receiver 0. All four codes 0100, 0101, 0110 and 0111 refer to receiver 1. The last two digits tell the receiver what action to take. Receiver 0, for example, responds to all signals beginning with 00, taking one of four possible actions, depending on the code contained in the final two digits. All other receivers ignore codes beginning with 00, and take no action. Another way of using this technique identifies up to 8 receivers by using the first 3 digits. The final digit then gives a simple 'on/off' control. Signal coding can also be extended to allow the use of several transmitters, each controlling one or more receivers. For example, all signals sent from transmitter 0 to receiver 0 begin with 00. All sent from transmitter 0 to receiver 1 begin with 01. All sent from transmitter 1 to receivers 0 and 1 begin with 10, and so on. The technique is very flexible. A similar technique may be used with PPM systems, using the i.c.s described on page 70.

The minimum requirement is two of these units, one as a transmitter and one as a receiver. If pin 3 (TX/RX) is made high, the unit transmits (Fig. 7.10a), otherwise it receives. It is possible to devise more complicated systems than that shown in the figure, in which the voltage at pin 3 can be switched on or off automatically, giving a two-way system. This could be useful if you require feedback from the controlled device. Note that the keyboard or coder used at the transmitter requires its own power supply (see Appendix D), as does the decoder and controlled device. Figures 5.5 and 5.6 show how to wire up the simplest possible input device — a single push button — for single-pulse or sequential-pulse control.

When building and testing these units it is strongly recommended that you take the mains power supply from a socket fitted with a residual current circuit breaker (RCCB). The same precaution applies to the next circuit.

The transceiver described above is very reliable, can transmit and receive a train of pulses at high speed, is highly immune from noise, but is complex to build and set up and is

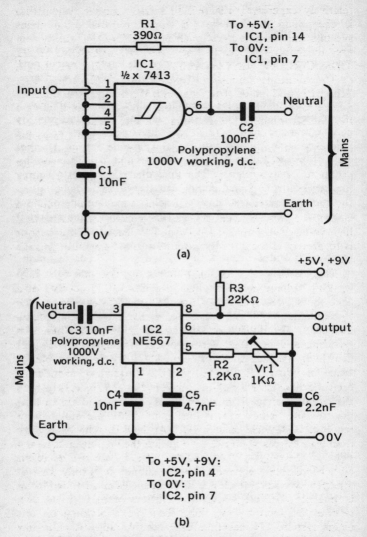

Fig. 7.11 Low-cost mains transmitter and receiver.

relatively expensive. Figure 7.11 shows a simple system that is cheap and is adequate for slow transmission on mains systems that do not have much noise. Note that the system uses the neutral and earth lines. **ON NO ACCOUNT MUST THIS CIRCUIT BE CONNECTED TO THE LIVE LINE.**

The transmitter consists of an oscillator built from a TTL Schmitt NAND gate. The frequency of the oscillator depends on the capacitance of C1. With the value shown in the figure the oscillator emits a tone burst of approximately 200kHz whenever the input to pin 1 goes high. The output from the oscillator is coupled to the neutral line by capacitor C2. This is a *polypropylene* capacitor of *high working voltage* (1000V). **CAPACITORS OF OTHER TYPES MUST NOT BE USED.** The voltage on the neutral line is normally close to that on the earth line, but should there be failure on electrical equipment connected to the mains, it is possible that high voltages may appear locally on the neutral. The capacitor is to prevent damage to the circuit, and the operator, in such circumstances.

The receiver, also coupled to the neutral line by a high working voltage *polypropylene* capacitor (C3) consists of a tone burst detector tuned to the same frequency as the transmitting oscillator. The i.c. used is the NE567 tone-decoder. The output of this i.c. is at pin 8. When it is receiving a tone burst of the correct frequency, the output goes low. The i.c. can operate on 5V or 9V, so is suitable for use with transistors, CMOS or TTL. It has an open-collector output so requires a pull-up resistor (Fig. 7.11b, R3) to hold the output voltage high when the i.c. is not receiving a tone burst. The values shown in Figure 7.11b are suitable for receiving a 200kHz tone burst. At 200kHz, the bandwidth is about 16% (as set by C5), so in fact the i.c. responds to any signal in the range 170 to 230kHz. The bandwidth decreases with increasing frequency. For example, it is only 11% at 400kHz. By suitable choice of frequencies and bandwidth, it is possible to have several transmitters, each with its own receiver(s) tuned to the same frequency operating on one mains system. To accommodate several transmitters, it may be necessary to reduce the bandwidth by increasing the value of C5. Increase the value of C4 too, so that it is approximately twice the capacitance of C5.

Special care is needed when designing and making the circuit boards, to ensure that no part of the circuit, except the 0V line and the mains side of C2 and C3, can come into contact with the mains lines. When testing the circuits it is not necessary to make connections to the mains. Simply connect their 0V lines together and join the output of the transmitter to the input of the receiver. The transmitter operates at a fixed frequency (f = 200/C1, approx., with C1 in microfarads), so it is necessary to tune the receiver to respond to it. To test the transmitter, observe its output using an oscilloscope. You should see a square wave, approximately 200kHz amplitude 5V. To test and adjust the receiver, connect a voltmeter to pin 8, and set the transmitter to produce a continuous tone (input high). The output from the receiver will probably be high (+5V or +9V) at this stage, if the tone is outside the range to which the receiver is tuned. Adjust VR1 *slowly* until the output voltage drops to 0V. The receiver is then tuned. Its output should rise to high again when the transmitter is not producing its tone. It may happen that no setting of VR1 will produce a low output. If so, replace R2 with a resistor of slightly lower or higher value.

Optical fibre
The main advantage of optical fibre is that it allows visible light or infra-red to be used for transmission over long distances with the minimum of noise. It is also useful in situations in which direct line-of-sight transmission is not convenient. The fibre is made from a polymer, and often coated in a black light-proof layer to prevent incident light from entering. Glass fibre is also available and has superior transmission properties, but is considerably more expensive than polymer fibre.

The signal from a filament lamp, visible-light LED or infra-red LED is passed into one end of the fibre and emitted from the other end. There it is detected by a suitable photo-sensor. The main consideration is that as much as possible of the radiation from the lamp or LED must enter one end of the fibre and as much as possible of the radiation

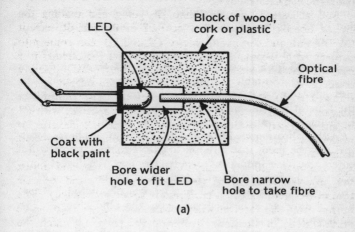

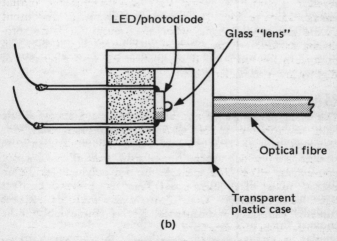

Fig. 7.12 (a) Section through home-made fibre-optic mount; (b) close-up section through 'Sweet Spot' device (simplified), mounting not shown.

reaching the far end must be directed at the photosensitive area of the sensor. To maximise the transfer of radiation the end of the fibre is sliced across at right angles with a sharp razor blade.

It is not difficult to improvise a mounting to hold the cut ends of the fibre close to the emitting and receiving devices (Fig. 7.12a). Suitable mounts are available ready-made. It is also important that extraneous radiation is not able to enter the fibre at the transmission end, or to reach the sensor at the receiving end, so it is essential that the mount is light-proof.

Although ordinary LEDs and photodiodes or phototransistors may be used, it is difficult to ensure that all the radiation enters the fibre and all is recovered from it. The 'Sweet Spot' series of devices comprises a high intensity infra-red LED, a visible light LED, and a Schmitt receiver photodiode. These have a tiny glass bead directly on the chip (Fig. 7.12b). Radiation from the emitting area of the LED is focussed by the bead into a narrow beam, most of which will enter the end of a fibre. Similarly, most of the radiation arriving at the receiving end of the fibre is focussed on to the sensitive area of the photodiode. Such devices are relatively more expensive than ordinary LEDs and photodiodes, but have applications when transmission is to take place over longer distances.

Radio

Details of radio construction and testing are outside the scope of this book. There are ready-made radio-control units available commercially which may be used in conjunction with the circuits described in this book. Or you may be able to remove the transmitter and receiver from a radio-controlled model that you no longer require. If you wish to build your own transmitter and receiver, the kits marketed by Maplin (see Appendix C) are relatively simple to construct. The way to connect these to remote control circuits is described below. Similar techniques may be employed with ready-made transmitters and receivers; it is hoped that the descriptions below will show you how to use these for remote control.

The Maplin 27MHz transmitter is assembled on a printed circuit board measuring 58mm x 48mm. It requires a power supply of 6V to 9V. Since its power consumption is only

15mA, it may be powered by a PP3 battery. This makes it very suitable for inclusion in a hand-held control unit. The p.c.b. has 8 terminal pins (Fig. 7.13), of which pins 5 and 7 are connected to the battery. The connection to the aerial comes directly from the aerial coil. The transmitter has 4 data channels, 2 for analogue data (Channels 1 and 2), and 2 for digital data (Channels 3 and 4), all of which operate simultaneously.

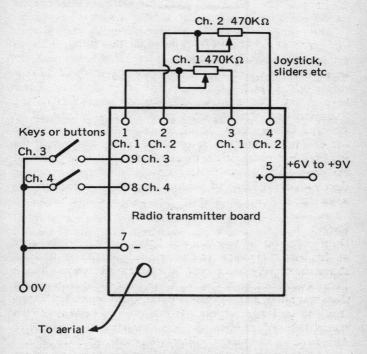

Fig. 7.13 Connections to the radio control transmitter.

The output from the transmitter consists of a 27MHz carrier wave fully modulated to produce a chain 6 pulses every 20ms (Fig. 7.14). The first two pulses are of variable length and convey the analogue information of Channels 1 and 2.

97

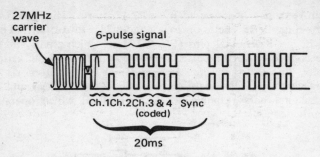

Fig. 7.14 Signal from the radio transmitter.

The other 4 pulses convey the coded logic level (low or high) information of Channels 3 and 4.

Analogue control of Channels 1 and 2 is by means of two rotary or slider potentiometers. The rotary potentiometers could be the two potentiometers of a proportional joystick. The full-track resistance of these should be 470k if the full range of output from the transmitter is to be achieved. The analogue information is conveyed by the width of the first two pulses. The effect of varying the resistance of VR1 or VR2 is to vary the width of the corresponding pulse.

The diagram (Fig. 7.13) shows two switches or push-buttons being used to input commands to Channels 3 and 4. This allows for the independent control of two on/off functions in the controlled device. The input pins of the transmitter may also be fed from the output of a TTL or CMOS gate. Thus Channel 3 or 4 can be used for transmitting pulses from a multiple-pulse coder or PPM coder. The only requirement is that the rate of pulse generation of the coder is appreciably slower than the rate of production of pulse trains by the coder in the transmitter. Since the latter produces a train every 20ms (50 times a second), while the pulses from the multiple-pulse coder last about 750ms, the two circuits are compatible.

Tone burst generator

The most convenient source for the high frequency is an astable multivibrator built from a 555 timer i.c., as in Figure

98

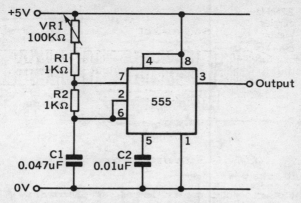

Fig. 7.15 Astable multivibrator using 555 timer IC.

7.15. The variable resistor is used for adjusting the frequency. With the values given, frequency can be adjusted over the range 300Hz to 10kHz. When a suitable frequency has been found, VR1 and R1 could be replaced by a single fixed resistor of the required value. The circuit could also be modified to allow switching of resistor value between the 5V line and pin 7, so as to allow the frequency to be set instantly to various values for controlling several devices from the same transmitter. An alternative way of providing a range of frequencies is to use one or more flip-flops to divide the frequency by 2 at each stage. A circuit for frequency division is shown in Figure 10.9. If the output from the 555 is fed to the input of this circuit, a waveform of half the frequency of the 555 is obtained from Output 1, and a waveform of one-quarter the frequency is obtained from Output 2.

The output from the 555 oscillator, or from any flip-flops connected to it, can be used directly to power an infra-red LED, as in Figure 7.16a. To drive a low-voltage filament lamp, use a transistor, as in Figure 7.16b. This allows transmission over greater distances (Chapter 6). The push-buttons are intended as 'transmit' buttons. When they are pressed a tone burst of infra-red radiation or visible light is transmitted. This is how these circuits are used in a single-pulse system or for sequential control (Chapter 5). For use in multiple-pulse

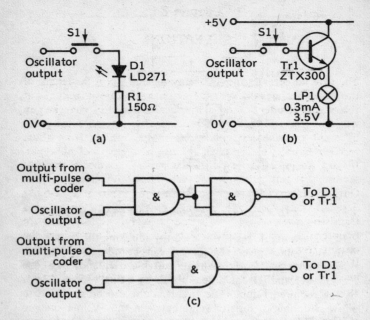

Fig. 7.16 Producing tone-bursts from an LED or filament lamp.

systems the circuits of Figure 7.16a and b are operated by logic gates. In the case of the multiple-pulse coder (Fig. 6.4) the output from the 555 must be ANDed with the output from the shift register of the coder. This may be done either with an AND gate or with two NAND gates, as shown in Figure 7.16c.

100

Chapter 8

RECEPTION

The type of receiver required may depend upon the length of the transmission path, and the amount of noise introduced at this stage. Under several of the headings in this chapter you will find a number of different receiving circuits suited to different transmission conditions. The outputs from these receiver circuits are suitable for use in systems of all types. If you are using tone-burst transmission, consult the last section of this chapter for tone-burst detecting circuits. Outputs from the receiver circuits, or from a tone-burst detector may be used in single-pulse systems to drive a transistor switch or to operate a relay, as described in Chapter 10. The same chapter also shows how to use the output from a receiver to operate a sequential-pulse system. If you are using a multiple-pulse system or PPM, you will need to pass the receiver output to an appropriate decoder, as described in Chapter 9.

Ultra-sound

The circuit of a simple, yet very effective, receiver is shown in Figure 8.1. The ultra-sound is picked up by the ultra-sonic receiver crystal, RX1. This is prepared during manufacture so as to resonate strongly to ultra-sound of frequency 40kHz. Thus it resonates strongly when it detects a signal from the transmitter described in Chapter 7, but is virtually unaffected by sounds of other frequencies. This gives freedom from spurious triggering of the circuit. The electrical output from the crystal is amplified by TR1 and TR2, rectified by D1, and produces a drop in the potential difference across R6 when a signal is being received. The operational amplifier, IC1, is affected by the consequent reduction in the current flowing to its inverting input (pin 2), and its output voltage (pin 6) rises. This raises the potential of both plates of C3, causing an increase of potential at the non-inverting input (pin 3), latching the i.c. to give continued high output. Eventually the additional charge on C3 is discharged through

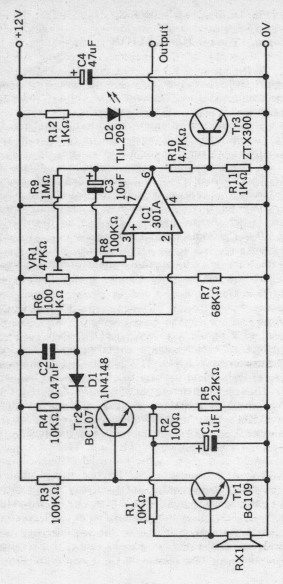

Fig. 8.1 Ultra-sonic receiver.

R9, and the i.c. becomes unlatched (assuming that the ultrasonic signal has ceased in the meantime), allowing the output to fall again. The variable resistor VR1 is used to set the level at which triggering of the circuit into latching condition occurs. If the value of C3 is increased to, say, 150μF, the latching action is prolonged for a period of about 10 seconds. This could be made use of if it was required that a short ultrasonic signal should evoke a prolonged response.

The output of IC1 is also fed to the potential-divider, R10/R11, so that TR3 is switched on when the output of the i.c. goes high. An LED can be used as shown to indicate the state of the circuit, the LED coming on when a signal has been received and going off a fraction of a second after the signal has ceased. The output of the circuit is taken from the collector of TR1, and is high (about 10.5V) when no signal is being received, dropping sharply to low (less than 0.1V) when a signal is detected. The values quoted apply to operation from a 12V supply, but it may be more convenient to operate the receiver from a battery giving 9V or 6V. Though this is lower than the voltage recommended for the i.c., this seems to make little difference to sensitivity and no changes in component values are required (though VR1 will need a different setting). If a 6V supply is used, the output voltage is 5V when high, and close to 0V when low, making the receiver completely compatible with TTL circuits. At 6V the receiver requires only 12mA, even when the LED is lit, thus making this circuit very suitable for battery operation in model control projects. Whether its output is analysed by TTL or, to obtain maximum power economy, by CMOS, depends on the kind of application. If CMOS is to be used, the PP3 battery is a conveniently small power supply, and both the receiver and CMOS i.c.s can operate on the 9V it supplies.

Construction

With reasonably compact layout the whole circuit can be accommodated on a piece of 0.1 inch matrix strip-board, about 15 strips wide and 30 holes long. This has room for an i.c. to analyse the output; if a more complex decoding circuit is required, the board should be larger or the decoder placed on a separate board. The receiver circuit presents no problems in assembly. The ultra-sonic receiver RX1 has two terminals, one of which is connected to its casing; this terminal should be connected to the ground line of the circuit. The whole circuit should be completed and checked for correct wiring, and the absence of solder bridges and other construction faults before it is tested. If the LED has been incorporated, this can be used to see if the circuit is working properly. If it has been decided not to include the LED, connect a voltmeter to the ground line and to the output terminal. When power is first applied the LED normally emits a single flash, though this may not happen at first testing. Instead the LED may shine continuously, indicating that the wiper of VR1 is set too near to the positive rail. If this is so, turn VR1 until the LED goes off; alternatively, if you are using a voltmeter across the output, turn VR1 until the voltmeter reads 'high'. The action of the receiver may then be tested by using the ultra-sonic transmitter (Chapter 7) held with its transmitter crystal pointing toward the receiver crystal and about 1 metre away from it. Immediately the 'transmit' button is pressed, the LED should light, and stay lit until a fraction of a second after the button has been released.

If the receiver shows no response, the fault probably lies with the transmitter, since its oscillator circuit (Fig. 7.1) may not be in perfect resonance with the transmitter crystal at exactly 40kHz. Adjust VR1 *of the transmitter* while pressing the 'transmit' button, until the receiver shows response by the lighting of the LED (or output voltage falls to zero). Then gradually increase the separation between transmitter and receiver, keeping the two crystals pointing at one another. Their effect is very directional and, though the system will work well even when they are not at all closely lined up, maximum range can be attained only when they are directed along the same axis. A range of 4m or more should be readily attainable, but much depends upon the nature of the surfaces of walls, floor and furniture. Range is relatively great in a narrow corridor, especially if it lacks carpets and curtains.

When you appear to have exceeded maximum range and the receiver no longer responds to transmissions, try adjusting VR1 of the transmitter to improve resonance. This may give even further extension of range. Try also to improve the sensitivity of the receiver by turning the wiper of VR1 (of the receiver) toward the positive rail until you reach a position in which the LED does not light, but from which position the slightest further movement toward the positive rail causes the LED to light. This is the position of maximum sensitivity.

See Figure 9.5 for a more sensitive receiver which demodulates the ultra-sonic signal, making it suitable for PPM systems.

Infra-red

A very simple yet useful receiver is shown in Figure 8.2.

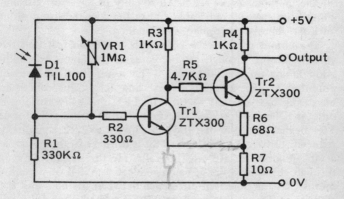

Fig. 8.2 Infra-red receiver interface.

It uses a photodiode that is sensitive in the infra-red range. The case of the diode is relatively opaque to visible light, though transparent to infra-red radiation. However, light from domestic filament lamps and high-intensity fluorescent lamps contains a strong component in the infra-red band. So does sunlight. If the circuit is to be used under brightly lit conditions, the action of the infra-red transmitter may be swamped. There are several ways to minimise this:

(i) Screen the photodiode from external sources as far as practicable.

(ii) Use a *strong* infra-red source in the transmitter – three, four or possibly more LEDs.

(iii) Place a colour-filter over the sensitive surface of the photodiode. Kodak filters 87 or 87C transmit infra-red and absorb most visible wavelengths; the 87C is slightly better in this respect.

(iv) Use a circuit that is sensitive only to sharply-defined pulses of infra-red, and not to gradual changes of intensity (see later).

(v) Use a tone burst circuit tuned to a particular frequency of modulation.

The methods above are listed roughly in order of cost and complexity, so it is advisable to try them in the listed order until satisfactory performance is obtained.

The circuit of Figure 8.2 depends upon the fact that the current passing through D1 increases as the amount of radiation falling on it is increased. The result is an increase of potential at the junction of D1 and R1. This causes an increasing base current to flow to TR1, gradually turning it on. As it becomes turned on, the potential at the collector of TR1 begins to fall, so that the base current to TR2 is gradually reduced, turning TR2 off. As TR2 is turned off, the potential at the junction of R6 and R7 falls, for the current flowing through these resistors is being reduced. A fall of potential means that the potential difference between the base and the emitter of TR1 is increased, so TR1 is turned more fully on. This turns TR2 even more fully off. A slight change of potential at the D1/R1 junction produces a rapid 'snap-action', turning TR2 off, and thus producing a 'high' output from the circuit. The level at which this transition occurs can be set by using VR1 to provide a given amount of bias current to TR1. VR1 is set so as to provide *almost* enough current to trigger the circuit. Any *additional* current resulting from a slight increase in the amount of radiation received will be sufficient to trigger the circuit, and cause its output to change from 'low' to 'high'.

Figure 8.3 shows a high-gain amplifier based on two operational amplifier i.c.s. Since the junction between D1 and R1 is coupled to the amplifier by a capacitor, the circuit responds to relatively *rapid changes* of irradiation, such as caused by the arrival of a pulse of infra-red, but not to slower changes

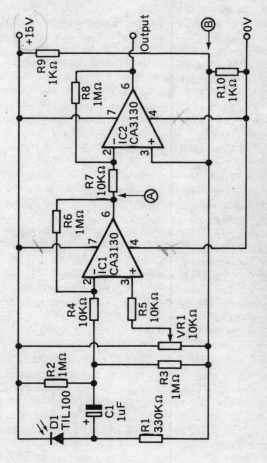

Fig. 8.3 Sensitive infra–red receiver.

107

such as *gradual changes* in the amount of sunlight reaching the sensor. By reducing the value of C1, this effect can be made even more distinct. The amplifier IC1 is connected as a differential amplifier; the variable resistor is set so that the output of this amplifier, as measured at point A is 7.5V with respect to the 0V rail. This resistor can be of the pre-set type.

It is also possible to operate this circuit without C1. If a wire link replaces C1, the circuit responds to all changes in radiation; the voltage at A goes negative for the duration of a pulse, and rises in between pulses. D1 and R1 may be interchanged if the reverse action is required. In this configuration VR1 may be a potentiometer (volume control) and used to set the level at which the circuit responds.

The single amplifier IC1 may be used on its own if the circuit is found to be sufficiently sensitive. For further amplification, the output from IC1 is fed to a second amplifier, connected as an inverting amplifier. The output from this swings strongly toward the positive rail when an infra-red pulse is received.

The output from these amplifiers, and the circuit next to be described may be used to drive transistors for switching operations (Chapter 10) or may be fed directly to CMOS gates, the CMOS i.c.s being powered from the +15V and 0V lines. Interfacing to TTL is more complicated because of the large voltage swings obtained from the amplifier output. One method of interfacing is given in Figure 8.4. The TTL circuit needs its own +5V supply, but the 0V line of this is connected to the 7.5V rail of the amplifier circuit, indicated by B in Figure 8.3. If the input voltage rises above +5.6V, with

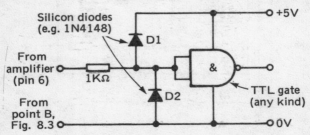

Fig. 8.4 Interfacing the infra-red receiver to TTL circuits.

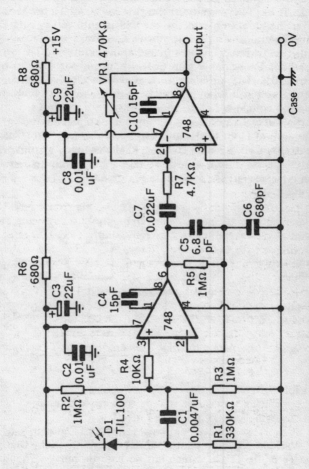

Fig. 8.5 High-gain amplifier for detecting infra-red radiation.

109

respect to the TTL ground line, D1 conducts and so the gate is protected and the input is received as a normal 'high' input. Conversely, if voltage falls below −0.6V, D2 conducts and the input is received as a normal 'low' input.

An even more sensitive receiving circuit is shown in Figure 8.5. It has two amplifiers, the first being connected as a non-inverting amplifier, and the second as an inverting amplifier. This circuit is coupled to the sensor by a capacitor, so is sensitive to rapid changes of radiation intensity. The second amplifier has variable gain (VR1) allowing for adjustment of sensitivity. One problem associated with the high gain of this circuit is that it is liable to pick up electrical interference from nearby equipment. It should therefore be housed in an earthed metal case, and the ground line connected to the case. The output from this circuit can be used for driving transistor switches, CMOS gates, and the PPM decoder. To drive TTL gates the maximum output voltage must be limited to +5V. An interface circuit is shown in Figure 8.6.

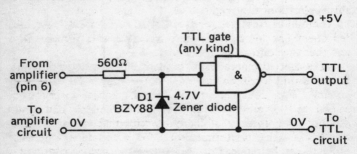

Fig. 8.6 Interfacing the high–gain amplifier to TTL circuits.

Visible light

The receiving transducer is a phototransistor, mounted behind a converging lens, as in Figure 7.4.

A short-range receiver circuit is shown in Figure 8.7

Various types of photo-transistor may be used. One such device is the TIL78, which has no base terminal. When using other types the base connection may be left unconnected as shown in Figure 8.7. If response is weak, a small base current

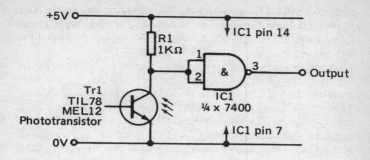

Fig. 8.7 Visible light receiver interface.

may be provided by connecting the base to the +5V line through a resistor of selected value. For higher sensitivity the photo-darlington transistor type MEL12 is highly recommended. This has a base terminal, which is left disconnected in this application, as in Figure 8.7.

The output from the receiver circuit of Figure 8.7 may be fed directly to the multiple-pulse register circuit of Figure 9.1 and thus the control link is complete.

At longer distances there is increased risk of changes in local lighting levels being sufficient to trigger the receiving circuit. For example, passing clouds, changes in shadows caused by the relative motion of the Sun, dusk, dawn, all produce slow changes of light intensity that can affect the response of the phototransistor. To a certain extent this problem can be reduced or even solved by careful positioning of transmitter bulb and phototransistor. If the transistor is already fully saturated with light, the small amount of additional light from the signal lamp will make no difference to its response. It is therefore essential to shade the phototransistor or its lens housing so that direct sunlight can not fall on it at any time of day. The transmitter bulb should not be placed against a large light-coloured surface, such as white painted wall because reflection from the wall at certain times of day may swamp the effects of the signal lamp. Even these precautions may be insufficient and the only solution is to use the slightly more elaborate receiving circuit shown in Figure 8.8.

111

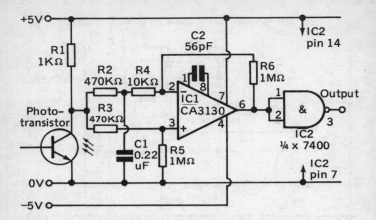

Fig. 8.8 Visible light receiver that responds only to rapid changes of intensity.

The collector of the phototransistor is connected to the inputs of an operational amplifier. The capacitor connected on the inverting-input channel damps voltage swings in that channel. If light intensity changes slowly, the effect of the capacitor is negligible; inputs are more-or-less equal and the output of the amplifier remains close to 0V, equivalent to logical 'low'. The output of the gate is therefore 'high'. However, if there is a *sudden* change in received light intensity, such as is caused by the arrival of a light signal, the imbalance at the two inputs is such as to cause a brief positive swing of the amplifier output. The result is a brief low pulse from the output of the gate. The ending of the light pulse has no significant effect in this circuit. Here we have a way of detecting the arrival of a signal pulse amid a background of slowly changing light levels. The low pulse from the gate (inverted if required) can be used to operate sequential control systems.

The multiple-pulse system requires that both the beginning and the end of the pulse should be detected. This is done by the circuit of Figure 8.9. In this circuit we detect the beginning of the pulse in the same way as in Figure 8.8. The end of the pulse is detected by a circuit in which the damping

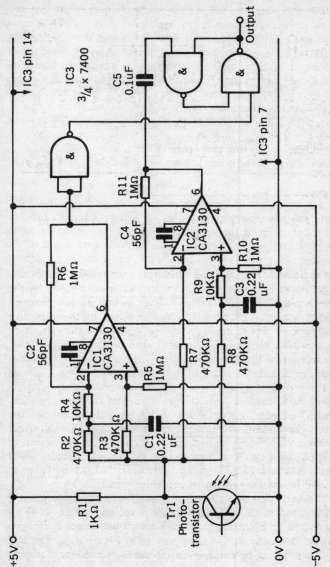

Fig. 8.9 Sensitive light-pulse detector.

113

capacitor is wired to the non-inverting channel (IC2). At the arrival of a pulse there is no significant change, but when a pulse ends, the output of the amplifier swings sharply negative of 0V. This negative pulse is transmitted through capacitor to one input of a bistable. The bistable is being used to reconstruct the original signal pulse by being *set* as the pulse begins and by being *reset* as it ends. The output from the bistable has approximately the same length as the original pulse and may then be fed to the register circuit of the multi-pulse system.

Wired link, mains link and optical fibre
Receivers for these systems have been described in Chapter 7.

Radio
As was explained in Chapter 7, the remote control radio transmitter and receiver marketed in kit form by Maplin Limited can be interfaced to many kinds of remote control system. Figure 8.10 shows the connections to the circuit board of the receiver. The digital outputs may be used directly for driving transistors or logic gates. They may be connected to decoders

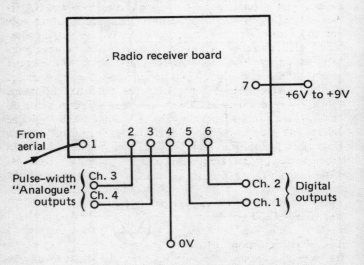

Fig. 8.10 Connections to the radio receiver.

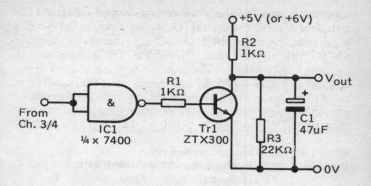

Fig. 8.11 Analogue output interface for the radio receiver.

(Chapter 9) or directly to controlled devices (Chapter 10). The analogue outputs deliver a square wave of fixed frequency but variable mark (high voltage) width. The circuit of Figure 8.11 is used to convert the output from Channels 3 or 4 into an analogue voltage. The output is inverted by the NAND gate so that when the output goes high, the gate output goes low and turns TR1 off. This gives a high voltage at the collector of TR1, charging C1 through R2. Part of the charge leaks away at a slower rate through R3. The longer the channel output is high, the longer TR1 is off and the more charge accumulates in C1. As a result, the potential difference across C1 ranges between about 0.7V and 4V, depending on the length of pulses from the channel output. This analogue voltage can then be used to control voltage-dependent devices. Note that the output impedance of the circuit is low. In other words, if an appreciable current is drawn from its output, the p.d. across C1 falls markedly. The output must therefore be fed to a high-impedance device, such as a field-effect transistor or an operational amplifier (see Figs 10.27 and 10.29).

Tone-burst detection

By using the circuit of Figure 8.12 the signal can readily be monitored by ear, assuming that the tone is in the audio-

115

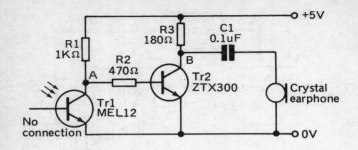

*Fig. 8.12 Simple receiver for tone-bursts
in an infra-red or visible light beam.*

frequency range. The values used in Figure 7.15 provide a range of tones, all of which are audible. This circuit is very useful when experimenting, and when setting up and testing an infra-red or visible-light link. Incidentally, the circuits of Figures 7.16a or b and 8.12 together make up a simple transmitter-receiver system for morse-code signalling by light-beam. Since this does not operate on radio-frequencies it is an entirely legal method of transmission and no licence is required. If, instead of using the 555 i.c., you take the output from an audio-amplifier, this system can be used to transmit speech or music.

In Figure 8.12, the transistor TR2 is being used to amplify the voltage changes occurring at point A when a signal is being received. To make an even simpler receiver, connect the earphone directly to point A, and omit TR2, R2 and R3. But for use with the detector circuit next to be described, amplification by TR2 is normally essential.

The essential features of a circuit that detects tone bursts of a particular frequency are shown in Figure 8.13. A voltage-controlled oscillator (VCO) is set to oscillate at a given frequency, the central frequency, which is the frequency to which we wish the circuit to respond. The frequency of the VCO is varied on either side of central frequency by varying the voltage applied to it from the loop filter. The phase comparator compares the input signal (which may come from a circuit like that of Figure 8.12) with the oscillations from

116

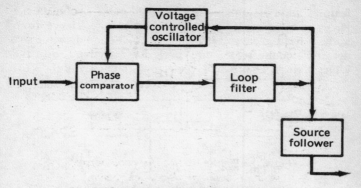

Fig. 8.13 Principle of a phase–locked loop.

the VCO. The output of the phase comparator is proportional to the error between the phase of the input signal and the phase of the signal from the VCO. This output is filtered by the loop filter. The varying voltage from the loop filter controls the frequency of the VCO making it change until it locks on to the frequency of the input signal. Thus the complete circuit, which is a closed loop, is known as a *phase-locked loop* (PLL). Output from the loop may be taken at several different stages, depending upon what functions are required. In the tone-burst-detecting application, output is taken from the loop filter, so as to monitor the control voltages being applied to the VCO. To minimise the loading on the loop filter, this voltage is not monitored directly, but though a source follower.

The complete circuit for a phase-locked loop is obtainable in a single CMOS i.c., the 4046. It needs only a few external capacitors and resistors. The i.c. contains two sections of the circuit as separate units: the VCO with source follower, and the phase comparator. Actually this i.c. contains *two* phase comparators, each with distinctive operating features. Phase comparator I is a low-noise phase detector (simply an exclusive OR gate), with a relatively narrow tracking range. It requires a 50% duty cycle for the input signal and also locks on to harmonics of the central frequency. Both of these

117

features are disadvantages in this application. Although the Phase comparator II is more subject to interference from noise it has the advantage of being a wide-band detector and does not require a 50% duty cycle for detection. With the values given in Figure 8.14, the central frequency of the VCO

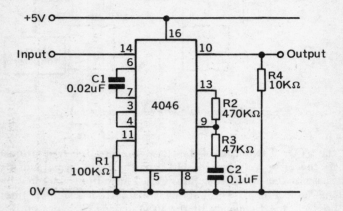

Fig. 8.14 Practical phase–locked loop circuit.

is approximately 300Hz. To work at other frequencies, C1 may be changed in value, since frequency is inversely proportional to capacitance. However, C1 must not be less than 100pF when supply voltage is 5V, or less than 50pF when supply voltage is 10V and over. Increasing R1 to 1MΩ reduces central frequency to approximately one-tenth, while reducing R1 to 10kΩ increases central frequency approximately tenfold. R1 must not be outside the range 10kΩ to 1MΩ. Central frequency is also increased approximately fifty-fold by increasing supply voltage to 10V or over. The loop filter consists of R2 and R3 with C2. With the values shown the circuit works as described and there is no need to alter these values.

The output from the source follower (pin 10) must be fed to a load resistor R4, which must have a minimum value of 10kΩ. The output may then be fed to a device of suitably high impedance (greater than 10kΩ) such as the input of a

118

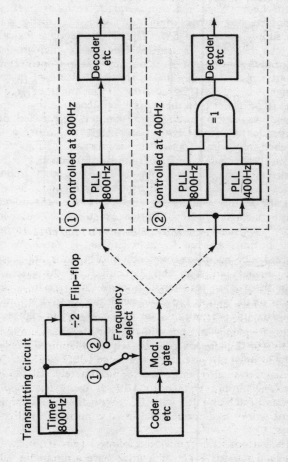

Fig. 8.15 Dual control from a single transmitter.

CMOS gate. When the input to the circuit is steady at 0V or at 5V (either of which conditions may be thought of as a signal of frequency 0Hz), output at pin 10 is low (0V). It remains close to 0V at input frequencies below the central frequency, though rises gradually as the central frequency is approached. When the input equals central frequency, the output reaches its maximum value, which is a little over 3V, at a supply voltage of 5V. This is effectively a logical high and can be fed to a CMOS logic gate. Increasing input frequency above central frequency has no further effect; output remains steadily high. Thus the output of the circuit is high whenever it is receiving a tone-burst or frequency equal to or higher than the central frequency.

One way of operating two remotely controlled devices independently from two transmitters or from a single switched-frequency transmitter is shown in Figure 8.15. Device 1 responds when the tone burst frequency is 800Hz because its phase-locked loop is tuned to that frequency. Device 2 responds when the tone-burst frequency is 400Hz, obtained in this example by dividing the timer frequency by 2, using a single flip-flop. Device 2 requires two phase-locked loops, one tuned to 400Hz and the other tuned to 800Hz. Their outputs are fed to an exclusive-OR gate. When the received tone-burst has frequency 800Hz, both loops respond, both outputs are high and the output of the gate is low. When there is no tone-burst, both outputs are low, and the output of the gate is low. But when the tone-burst frequency is 400Hz, the outputs of one loop (400Hz) is high and the other one (800Hz) is low; this is the exclusive-OR condition, and the output of the gate goes high, thus passing the pulse to the decoder.

Chapter 9

DECODING

Decoders are not required for single-pulse and sequential pulse systems. If you are designing such a system, circuits for the next and final stage of your system are described in Chapter 10.

Multiple-pulse 4-digit decoder

This circuit (Fig. 9.1) is designed to decode transmissions coded by the 4-digit coder described in Chapter 6. Every command pulse train consists of a half-length 'start' pulse, followed by four full-length code pulses. These may each be high or low depending on the coding.

When the 'start' pulse arrives at the receiver, it causes the trigger pulse generator to produce one very short low-going pulse that triggers the 555 timer (IC2) into action. The relationships between the various pulses of this circuit is illustrated in Figure 9.2. By reading from left to right across the diagram we can follow the various stages of operation. The top line of the diagram represents the command pulse train arriving at the receiver. The 'start' pulse is shown high (S), the code pulses, d, c, b, a, (transmitted in that order) may be low or high, and are followed by a low state that lasts until the next command train arrives. In the second line of the diagram we see the brief trigger pulse which occurs on the leading edge of the 'start' pulse. There are other trigger pulses later (indicated by '?') if a low pulse in the code is followed by a high one, but these have no effect once the 555 has been triggered. The 555 is connected as a monostable multivibrator and its output goes high until halfway through the pulse representing digit a.

The output from the timer is fed to a double-pulse generator that produces a high 'count' pulse as the timer output goes high and a high 'stop' pulse as the timer output goes low (Fig. 9.2). The 'count' and 'stop' pulses are on separate lines. The purpose of the 'count' pulse is to synchronise the clocking of the shift register in this circuit with the clocking of the shift

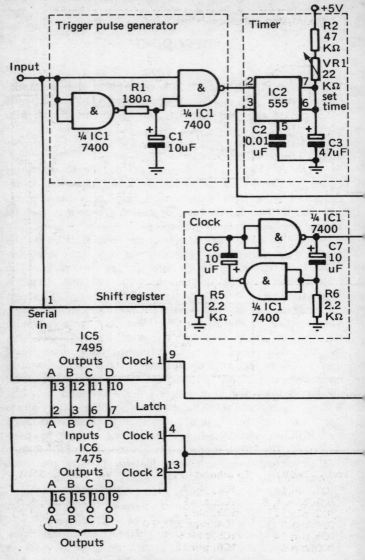

Fig. 9.1 Multiple-pulse decoder (4-digit).

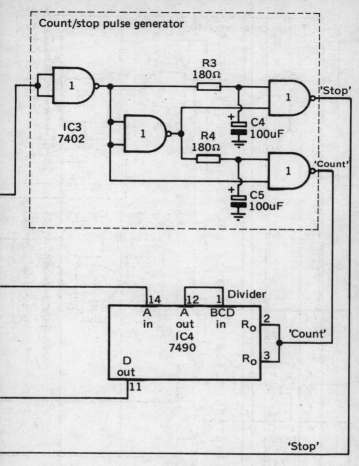

To V_{cc} (+5V):
   IC1, pin 14
   IC2, pins 4, 8
   IC3, pin 14
   IC4, pin 5
   IC5, pin 14
   IC6, pin 5

To ground (0V):
   IC1, pin 7
   IC2, pin 1
   IC3, pin 7
   IC4, pins 6, 7, 10
   IC5, pins 6, 7
   IC6, pin 12

To V_{cc} through 1KΩ
resistor:
   IC5, pins 2, 3, 4, 5
   (parallel inputs)

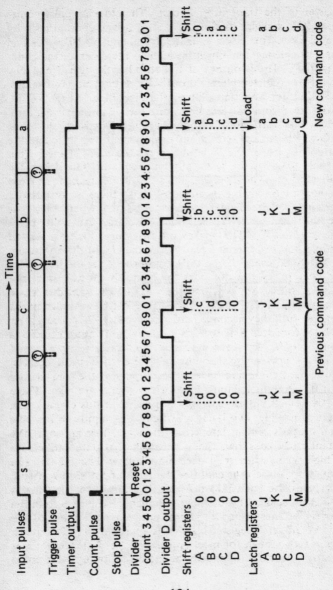

Fig. 9.2 Waveforms of the multiple-pulse decoder circuit.

124

register of the transmitter circuit. The clocking pulse comes from IC4, a divide-by-ten i.c. that is driven continuously by the clock. The clock is made from two NAND gates and has a frequency ten times faster than the clock of the coder (Fig. 6.4). The D output of IC4 thus has the same frequency as the transmitter clock, though its duty-cycle is different, being low for four times longer than it is high. At the 'count' pulse the divider is reset and continues counting from zero. Since the 'start' pulse is only half the length of the code pulses, it reaches zero again exactly half-way through the period of each of the code pulses. As the count changes from 9 back to zero, the D output falls, and this fall clocks the shift register. The diagram shows the divider being reset from a count of 6, when D is already low, so there is no pulse on resetting. If the divider is at counts 8 or 9 when it is reset, the shift register is clocked, and this shifts the 'start' pulse into register A. This makes no difference, for it is shifted through the registers and lost before the end of the operation.

The serial input of the shift register receives the start pulse and code pulses directly from the circuit input and, since the clocking pulses are synchronised to coincide with the centre of each code pulse, the code pulses are shifted as shown in the diagram until they each are held in a register. This occurs after 4 shifts (or after 5 if there is an initial shift due to resetting from 8 or 9). The code must next be transferred to a second set of registers where it can be held (or latched) until replaced by the next command code. The outputs of the four latches of IC6 follow their inputs if the clock inputs are high. There are two clock inputs, operated in parallel in this circuit, each input controlling two latches. When clock inputs go low, the latch outputs remain latched in the state they are in at the instant clock goes low. They remain in that state until clocks go high again, when they once more follow their inputs. The brief 'stop' pulse thus captures the state of the shift registers. This loads the code into the latch registers, where it remains until it is replaced by the next command. The time from the pressing of the 'transmit' button until the appearance of the code at the latch register outputs is approximately 3 seconds. This is fast enough for most applications. If faster response is essential the clock rates may be increased, though this could lead to difficulties in adjusting the system and might make it more susceptible to mis-timing should the values of electrolytic capacitors change, as they often do with age, especially when left unused for a period.

Construction

The unit requires only 6 i.c.s together with a few other components, so can easily be accommodated on a small circuit-board. The prototype used a piece of strip-board 50 holes long and 18 strips wide, the i.c.s being arranged in two rows of 3. The circuit can be powered from a 5V regulated power-pack, or from a 6V battery.

First assemble the clock, using two of the gates of IC1. Next connect the divider (IC4), remembering to ground the two 'Reset 9' inputs (pins 6 and 7). Temporarily ground the two 'Reset 0' inputs (pins 2 and 3) so that the clock and divider can be tested. Outputs are most conveniently tested by connecting them to an LED in series with a 180 ohm resistor which is itself connected to ground. Connect an LED to the D output of the divider; it should flash regularly, about 15 times in 10 seconds (1.5Hz). If another LED is connected to the output of the clock in the transmitter, this should be seen to flash at the same rate. The rate of the transmitter clock should now be adjusted, using VR1 *of the coder*, until the two LEDs flash at equal rates, as near as can be judged by watching them. Since the transmission cycle occupies only 4 clock pulses, slight discrepancies are of no importance.

Next build the trigger pulse generator, using the two gates remaining unused in IC1. Wire up IC2 and the connection between it and the trigger pulse generator. The trigger pulse is too short to be observed using an LED, but its action can be checked by testing the output of the timer. Immediately a high pulse is applied to the circuit input, the timer output should go high and remain high for approximately 3 seconds. Adjustment of the timer pulse length will be done later.

The count/stop pulse generator uses all 4 NOR gates of a 7402 i.c. The values of C4 and C5 are not critical; any surplus capacitors with values between $22\mu F$ and $150\mu F$ can be used. Connect 2 LEDs to this generator to check its action (see Fig. 9.2). Next connect the 'count' output to the 'Reset 0' input of IC4. Now an LED connected to the D output should flash regularly, except when the arrival of a high pulse at circuit input causes the timer to operate and to generate the 'count' pulse that resets IC4. This shows as an interruption in the regularity of the flashing rate. It should resume flashing regularly about 0.7 seconds later. If an LED is connected to the timer output, we are ready to adjust the length of the timer pulse. Simply apply a high pulse to the circuit input; timer output should go high immediately and stay high until *just after the* fourth flash from the LED connected to divider D output. Adjust VR1 *(receiver)* until the timer LED goes out just after the fourth flash of the divider LED.

Complete the circuit by connecting the shift register and latch i.c.s, and it will then be ready for final testing. For this, remove all test LEDs from the circuit, and then connect four LEDs to the latch outputs. Connect the output of the coder by wire to the input of the receiver. Power both coder and receiver from the same source for the purposes of testing. When the circuit is switched on, one or more of the LEDs may light, at random. Select control position '4' (= binary 0100; so $c = 1$, $a = b = d = 0$). Press the 'transmit' button. About three seconds later the LED connected to register C should light, and the other three LEDs should be dark. If more than one LED is lit, something is wrong with the timing (you may be catching the 'start' pulse), or with the wiring associated with the control switch, the shift registers or the latch. If one LED lights but it is the one connected to latch B, this indicates that latching has occurred *before* the final fourth shift. Lengthen the timer pulse by adjusting VR1 of the receiver. Conversely, if the D LED lights, reduce the length of the timer pulse. At each adjustment, press 'transmit' to repeat the test. Next select control position '9' (= binary 1001; so $a = d = 1$, $b = c = 0$) and repeat the test. If LEDs A and D light this is a sure indication that the pulse train has reached exactly the correct registers at the time of latching. Finally run through all control positions to check for correct action. The receiver is now ready to be connected to a decoder designed to interpret the command codes and relay corresponding instructions to the controlled device. Details of how this is done are given in Chapter 10.

Multiple-pulse 8-digit decoder

This circuit is almost identical to that of the 4-digit coder, except that the shift register and latch i.c.s are for 8 digits instead of 4. The principle of operation of the circuit is exactly the same. Figure 9.3 shows how 74164 and 74273 i.c.s are substituted for the 7495 and 7475 i.c.s of Figure 9.1. The length of time between the 'count' pulse and the 'stop' pulse must be doubled to allow 8 pulses to be received. The

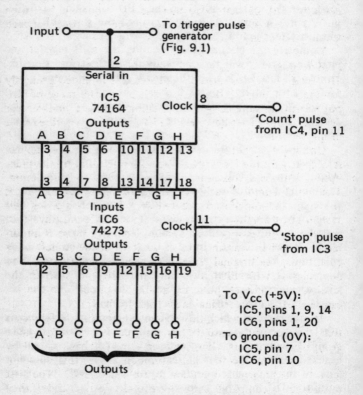

Fig. 9.3 Multiple–pulse decoder for 8–digits.
The remainder of the circuit is the same as in Fig 9.1,
except that C3 has the value 100uF.

value of C3 is increased to $100\mu F$ to double the length of time for which the timer output is high.

Building and setting up the system is the same as described in the previous section, except that you need 8 LEDs to connect to the outputs of the latch i.c. Having checked the operation of the circuit at slow speed, in which the pulse rate is 1.5Hz, the coder may be adapted as described earlier, to operate at ten or more times this rate. The decoder must be similarly adapted. Replace capacitors C6 and C7 of the clock by $1\mu F$ capacitors to increase its frequency. Replace the C3 by a $4.7\mu F$ capacitor to reduce the time between 'count' and 'clear'.

PPM decoders

The PPM coder described in Chapter 6 is intended primarily for use with the 922 decoder, which provides a range of output facilities suitable for controlling TV sets and similar devices. Four other decoders, 926 to 929, are described later in this section.

One great advantage of the system is that the decoder i.c. is triggered by the *leading edge* of each pulse, not by the pulse itself. This is a consequence of pulse position modulation. The actual *length* of each pulse does not matter (provided it is less than the time-interval between pulses), thus giving this system great immunity from noise. In multiple-pulse systems, and the digital proportional system, length of pulse is important and, when transmission is weak or made under noisy conditions, the original signal may become so distorted as to be useless. With PPM it is only necessary to sharpen the leading edge of each pulse by a suitable circuit and the i.c. can reconstruct the original pulse train for itself.

Another way in which this system overcomes interference is that the i.c. waits until it has received two *identical* pulse groups before it acts. If there is an error (perhaps caused by interference) in the first pulse train to arrive, this does not lead to an incorrect operation being performed. The first pulse train is compared with the second to arrival and, *if* they are identical, action is taken. If not, the i.c. rejects the first, awaits the third train and compares this with the second, and so on. Under bad reception conditions this could cause a slight delay in response but this is preferable to wrong functions being activated and is a warning that perhaps the control operation should be terminated.

The i.c. is connected as in Figure 9.4. The frequency of the internal clock is determined by the values of C1, VR1 and R2, according to the equation:

$$f = \frac{1}{0.15C_1 (R_1 + R_2)}$$

where VR1 has value R_1 and R2 has value R_2. $R_1 + R_2$ must lie between $25k\Omega$ and $200k\Omega$. It is to be adjusted in value so that $f = 40/t_0$, t_0 being the time for a '0' interval, as explained in Chapter 6. C2 and R3 determine the time taken for the 'initial' conditions of outputs (see later) to be set up following the switching on of the i.c. The values given make this period 2 second. C3 and R4 determine the *step time constant*. This determines how rapidly the program outputs are stepped through their sequence of programs when the 'program step' (+ or −) command is received. The program outputs can also be made to step by a switching action at the receiver. If pin 5 is grounded, the program outputs step through their sequence, cycling continuously at the rate determined by the step time constant. This function could be remotely controlled by using one of the analogue outputs.

The analogue outputs each produce a current that is a given fraction of the reference current, I_{ref}. The value of I_{ref} is determined by resistor R5. With the value shown, I_{ref} is between 250 and $450\mu A$. At switch-on (initial conditions) the current from analogue outputs is 12/8 of I_{ref}, that is to say somewhere in the range 375 to $675\mu A$, and with the loads represented by the $3.9k\Omega$ resistors the voltages at these outputs are in the range 1.5V to 2.6V. As the 'analogue +' command is transmitted, output currents increase in steps of 1/8 of I_{ref} up to a maximum value of 31/8 of I_{ref}. As the 'analogue −' command is transmitted, the output currents decrease by steps of 1/8 of I_{ref} to zero.

The program outputs are listed in the table following. As can be seen, they are simply the inverse of the corresponding program number, in binary form:

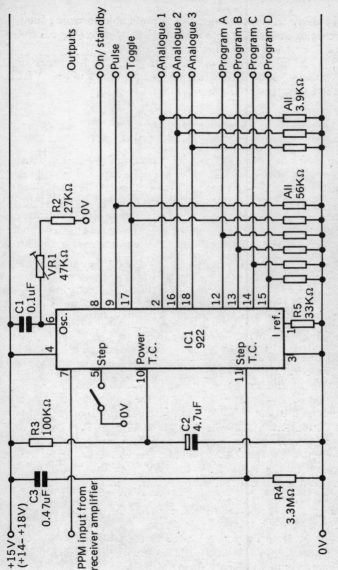

Fig. 9.4 Connecting the 922 decoder IC.

131

Program number	Outputs			
	A	B	C	D
0	H	H	H	H
1	H	H	H	L
2	H	H	L	H
3	H	H	L	L
4	H	L	H	H
5	H	L	H	L
6	H	L	L	H
7	H	L	L	L
8	L	H	H	H
9	L	H	H	L

L = low   H = high

The way of feeding signals to the decoder i.c. depends on the transmission method employed. It is possible to use line transmission of commands, in which case a low-value capacitor should be used between the terminal of the line and the input to the decoder. A $0.001\mu F$ capacitor is suitable. In this application, there is no carrier frequency, so the coder is without C1, and a fixed resistor $2.2k\Omega$ is used in place of R1 (see Fig. 6.9). For infra-red and visible-light transmission a high-gain amplifier such as that shown in Figure 8.5 can be used.

With ultra-sonic transmission the circuit of Figure 9.5 provides for demodulation of the signal to make it suitable for the receiver i.c.

If the analogue conversion and other special features of the 922 are not required (most of which are geared to using the decoder in a TV remote control system), it is more convenient to use one of the 926–929 receivers. These each respond only to 16 of the 32 code groups produced by the 490 transmitter. The 926 and 928 respond to groups 00000 to 01111, while the 927 and 929 respond to groups 10000 to 11111. Thus the keyboard can have up to 32 keys, corresponding to all positions on the matrix of Figure 6.9. The 926 or 928

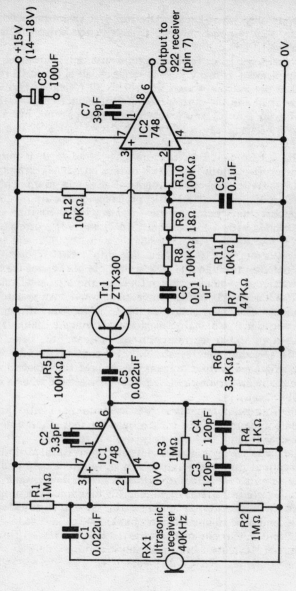

Fig. 9.5 Ultrasonic receiver amplifier.

133

responds only when keys in the top 4 rows are pressed; the 927 or 929 respond only when keys in the bottom 4 rows are pressed.

If you have 16 or fewer functions, use only 1 decoder i.c. and implement as many keys as required, all in the top 4 rows or all in the bottom 4 rows. For 17 to 32 functions two i.c.s are required and the corresponding keys in up to 8 rows. It is possible to control two independent devices from one keyboard by having, say a 926 in one device and a 927 in the other.

The 926 and 628 differ from each other in their output characteristics. Both i.c.s have 4 output terminals corresponding to the 4 least significant digits of the code group. Thus a code group such as 01010, produces the output 1010. Remember that these i.c.s use negative logic, so that a '0' corresponds with a high output (15V) and a '1' corresponds with a low output (0V). Similarly, with the 927 and 929, the code group 11010 produces the output 1010. The difference between the 926 and 928 is that the outputs of the 926 are unlatched, whereas the outputs of the 928 are latched. The 927 and 929 differ in the same way. An unlatched output appears only as long as the i.c. is receiving the signal. When no signal is being received the outputs are 0000. Thus the output 0000 corresponds to 'absence of signal' so strictly speaking, the 927 and 929 respond only to 15 codes. With a latched output the output is held unchanged, even when no signal is being received, and changes only when a new signal is received.

The four outputs of these i.c.s can be used to control just 4 separate functions, one for each output. This is the simplest arrangement and requires only driving transistors or other devices (see Chapter 10) to activate the controlled devices. Each output can provide up to 15mA, so can be used to drive LEDs, thyristor controlled opto-electronic devices and the like. To control a greater number of functions, the outputs are fed to a decoder, as in Figure 10.31. This shows the i.c. being used as a 10-line decoder, but the 4514 and 4515 have 16 output lines. The output pins for program lines 10 to 15 are 6, 7, 8, 10, 9, and 11 respectively.

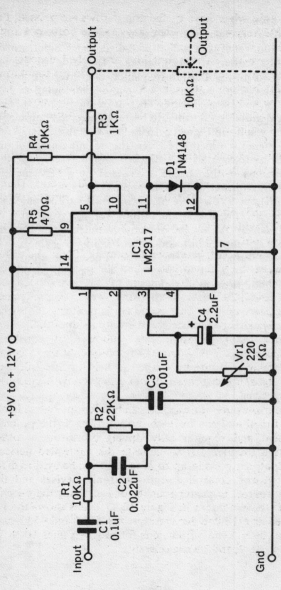

Fig. 9.6 Frequency-to-voltage converter. Dotted lines show how to obtain a lower output voltage, using a potential divider.

135

Analogue decoding

The decoding of analogue signals generated by a digital A-to-D converter connected to a 4-digit or 8-digit coder is performed as described earlier in this chapter. Decoding of signals originating from a voltage-to-frequency converter requires a frequency-to-voltage converter. A circuit employing such a converter is shown in Figure 9.6. It requires only a few milliamps to run it, so is suited to battery-powered equipment. Using the circuit of Figure 5.16 in the transmitter and the circuit of Figure 9.6 in the receiver, the output voltage of the receiver is approximately 1.2 times the input voltage at the transmitter. When the circuit is powered by a 10V supply, the maximum output voltage is approximately 6V. If the supply voltage is 9V, a value more convenient to obtain with battery power, the maximum output voltage is about 5V. Over the range 0V to the maximum output voltage the relationship between input and output voltages is linear. If you wish the output voltage to be the same as the input, the output can be reduced by feeding it to a potential divider (see dotted modification to circuit).

Chapter 10

THE OUTPUT INTERFACE

At this point, the chain of remote command has nearly reached
its end. Now the command is to be passed to the controlled
device itself. The chapter begins by considering what can be
done with the simplest type of control system, the single-
pulse system, and then goes on to look at the more complicated types of control of the other systems. It ends by
describing some more specialized forms of control.

Single-pulse control

The single pulse may be used either to switch a device on for
as long as the pulse lasts, or to trigger a device into action.
If the device is triggered into action, it continues its action
after the pulse has ended. This action could, of course,
consist of several distinct stages controlled by electrical
circuits or by mechanisms within the device itself.

The easiest way to switch a device on or off for as long
as the pulse lasts is to use a transistor as a switch. This
method is applicable to devices that operate at relatively
low voltage, and use direct current.

The current available at the collector terminal of a transistor depends on how much current the transistor can safely
conduct when switched on. In Figure 10.1a, all current
passing through the load also passes through the transistor.
The maximum current allowed is a few hundred milliampere
if the transistor is of the low-power type. If the load requires
only a low current it may be necessary to connect a resistor
in series with the load to limit the current flowing. If a
current greater than a few hundred milliamperes is required,
we simply substitute a transistor of higher power rating.
Examples are the BD131, which can handle up to 3A, and the
2N3055 which takes up to 15A. The circuit in Figure 10.1a
powers the load when the transistor is switched on (high
input). The circuit of Figure 10.1b powers the load when the
transistor is switched off (low input). When the transistor is
on, all or most of the current flows through the transistor,

137

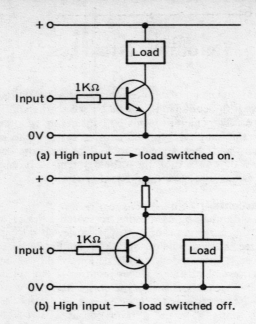

(a) High input ⟶ load switched on.

(b) High input ⟶ load switched off.

Fig. 10.1 Using a transistor as a switch.

by-passing the load. There is still a current flowing through the load, though normally this is small, for the effective resistance of the switched-on transistor is much less than the resistance of the load. If the load is a lamp, the current may be insufficient to make the filament glow. With other kinds of load even a small current may be unacceptable; the solution is to use the switching circuit of Figure 10.1a, but with an inverted input. If a spare logic gate is available this may be used to invert the load. If not, a transistor can be used as inverter as in Figure 10.2.

TTL i.c.s can not be operated above 6V, but if a load requires higher voltage, it can be fed from a separate supply, as in Figure 10.3. Both sides of the circuit share a common 0V rail. The voltage on the load side must not exceed the maximum collector-emitter rating (V_{CEO}) of the transistor. When

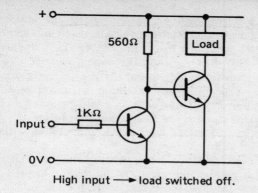

High input ⟶ load switched off.

Fig. 10.2 Another transistor switch.

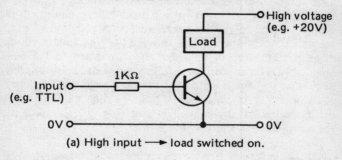

(a) High input ⟶ load switched on.

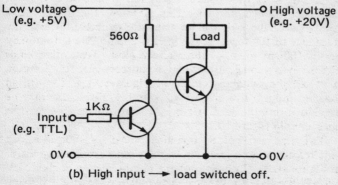

(b) High input ⟶ load switched off.

Fig. 10.3 Switching a load that operates from a higher voltage.

using high voltages, high currents, or both, the maximum power rating of the transistor must also be taken into account. Typical values are 300mW for the ZTX300, 15W for the BD131 and 90W for the 2N3055. When operated at high power the transistors must normally be mounted on an adequate heat-sink. The only exception is if the transistor is switched on only briefly and with long 'off' periods between. Then the small quantity of heat generated during the 'on' period has time to escape during the 'off' period, without need for a heat-sink.

A precaution must be taken when switching *inductive* loads, such as motors, bells, buzzers and relays. In these the current passes through one or more electromagnetic coils. When current is switched off, the sudden collapse of the magnetic field causes a high e.m.f. to be induced in the coils. This e.m.f. may be tens of volts in magnitude, even though the supply current to the load was well below 10V. The e.m.f. causes a high current to flow through the coils and, of course, through transistors or i.c.s that are connected to the coils. Since the induced current is always in a direction *opposite* to that of the supply current it can do a great deal of damage in an instant. To guard against this we connect a diode across the terminals of any inductive load (Fig. 10.4). This discharges the reverse current safely.

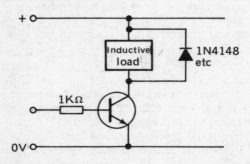

Fig. 10.4 Protective diode in use with an inductive load.

Mention of relays reminds us that here is yet another means of switching power to heavy loads. Relays are relatively

140

expensive, bulky and slow-acting compared with transistors but, for heavy loads or when the load is to be driven by alternating current, a relay is to be preferred. Figure 10.5 shows the complete circuit of an ultra-sonically controlled relay. This could be used for controlling room lighting or for switching on any other mains-powered device, such as a radio set, an electric fan, or a film projector. The use of a flip-flop (4027) gives it toggle action: press 'transmit' to switch on; press again to switch off. By suitable choice of relay, this circuit could be used to switch on one device while simultaneously switching off another. Wired between the pick-up cartridge and amplifier of a hi-fi system, the circuit could be used for instantly muting the system when, for example, a telephone call has to be made. In this application a heavy-duty relay is not required. Instead one could use one of the small relays in 14-pin d.i.l. cases (the same size and shape as a TTL or CMOS i.c.). These can be used to switch voltages up to 100V and currents up to 0.5A. Their small size makes them particularly convenient for model-control circuits and it is convenient to be able to mount them on the same circuit-board as the i.c.s. Another advantage is that they can be powered directly by the output of a standard TTL gate. One brand of d.i.l. relay has the protecting diode already built-in, but it is wise to check for this feature before using relays of other makes.

The circuit of Figure 10.5 illustrates the chief features of a circuit for controlling a device that operates on relatively high voltage or with alternating current. Other receiver circuits, or a receiver circuit plus tone-burst detector could be inserted in place of the ultra-sonic receiver. If the output from the receiver is from a multi-pulse decoder, it can feed signals to several other 4027 i.c.s, so switching a number of other devices on and off remotely (see later).

Another type of transistor suitable for power switching is the VMOS power transistor. This has the virtue of being able to switch large currents. Also its resistance is negligible when it is switched on, making all of the supply voltage available for driving the controlled device. Figure 10.6 shows how to use such a transistor as a switch. This circuit switches currents up to 2A, with a maximum supply voltage of 60V. It requires

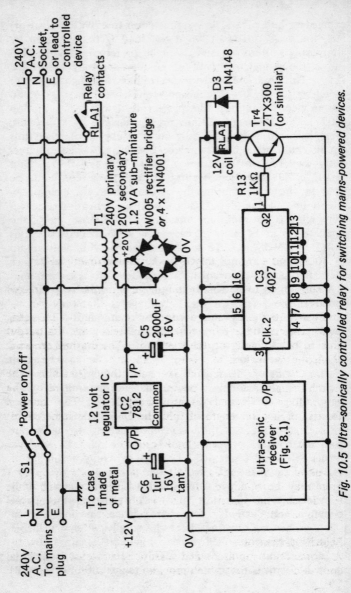

Fig. 10.5 Ultra-sonically controlled relay for switching mains-powered devices.

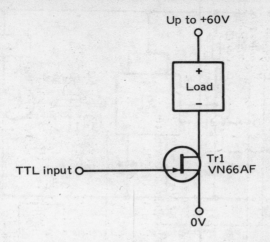

Fig. 10.6 Using a VMOS power transistor as a switch.

a heat sink if used for switching large currents for prolonged periods.

Figure 10.7 illustrates a trigger circuit. A low incoming pulse triggers the 555 monostable multivibrator. Its output goes high, switching on the transistor. The diagram shows it triggering the switch of Figure 10.1a, but the switches from Figure 10.1b to 10.4 could be substituted for this. The switch remains on for a period of time determined by the capacitance of C1 and the resistance of R1. The equation for calculating the length of time the device is switched on is:

$$t = 1.1 \times R \times C$$

By using suitable values for C1 and R1, periods of up to 1 hour may be obtained. If a second pulse is received while the device is in operation, this has no effect on the original timing period.

Sequential control

A commonly required and easily constructed sequential control circuit is that which provides toggle action (Fig. 10.8).

143

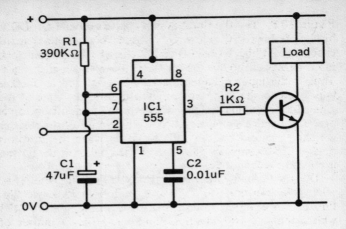

Fig. 10.7 Pulse–triggered transistor switch.

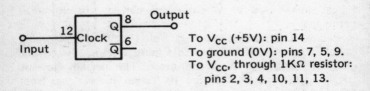

To V_{cc} (+5V): pin 14
To ground (0V): pins 7, 5, 9.
To V_{cc}, through 1KΩ resistor:
  pins 2, 3, 4, 10, 11, 13.

Fig. 10.8 Using a single JK flip–flop to provide toggle action.

This has an input which may be connected to the output of a receiver or decoder, a transistor switch, a relay, or further logic circuits, as will be described later. The circuitry of the device itself, which is called a J-K flip-flop, is not shown as we are not concerned with the internal details of its working. One input to this flip-flop is called 'clock' and there are other inputs which we are not using in this application. The unused inputs are connected to the positive rail (5V, V_{cc}) through a 1 kilohm resistor, to hold them permanently at 'high' level. Only one resistor is used, one end being connected to the 5V rail, the other end being connected to all the pins listed in

144

Figure 10.8. The flip-flop has two outputs, Q and Q̄: if Q is high, Q̄ is low; if Q is low, Q̄ is high. When the clock input changes from high to low, Q and Q̄ change state. When clock input changes from low to high, the outputs remain unchanged. Thus if the input is connected to a receiver and an LED is connected to the Q output of the flip-flop, the state of the LED (lit or not lit) changes whenever the transmit button is pressed. By this simple addition to the circuit of the receiver we have arranged for the LED to go on when the button is pressed and *to stay on*, for hours if need be, until the button is pressed a second time.

The next step is to connect two flip-flops in series (Fig. 10.9). We can use two 7470 i.c.s, each with its single flip-flop or, for economy in cost, space and wiring, use the 7473 which contains two identical flip-flops. The Q output of

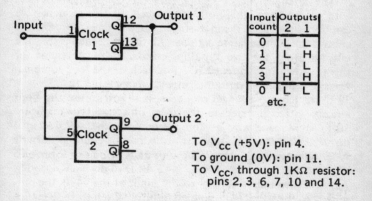

To V_{CC} (+5V): pin 4.
To ground (0V): pin 11.
To V_{CC}, through 1KΩ resistor: pins 2, 3, 6, 7, 10 and 14.

Fig. 10.9 Sequential controller, using a 7473 dual JK flip-flop.

flip-flop 1 is fed to the clock input of flip-flop 2. As before, outputs change state whenever clock inputs go low. The effect of this is to produce the sequence shown in the table in Figure 10.9. There are four stages to this sequence, and the outputs change each time the 'transmit' button is pressed.

Electronic circuits of this type are very similar in function to the mechanical arrangements formerly used for remote control, and still used in cheap radio-controlled toys. In these there is some kind of ratchet mechanism which is actuated each time a radio pulse is received. At the mechanism turns, step by step, it brings various gear-wheels or levers into action, so the model goes through a sequence of actions. For example, a toy 'robot' might be made to move forward, turn left, turn right, stop, in sequence. If it is moving forward and you want it to turn right, you press the button twice in rapid succession, so that it skips past the 'turn left' stage very quickly. Similar escapement mechanisms driven by twisted rubber were former-ly widely used in model aeroplanes. We can use the same approach with the flip-flop circuit of Figure 10.9, so that when controlling two motors we can have neither, one, the other, or both running, and can skip from one state to the other by pressing the button rapidly the appropriate number of times.

The arrangement of Figure 10.9 can control two devices with a 'none-one-other-both' sequence. In this sequence we can recognise four distinct stages, so we have the basis for controlling four separate actions. All that is needed is that the outputs from the two flip-flops are *decoded*. A circuit for this is shown in Figure 10.10. For each of the four combina-tions of inputs, *one* output channel goes high.

If we require a longer sequence, it is best to use flip-flops already interconnected in the form of a counter i.c. Figure 10.11 shows one way of doing this, using the 7490 decimal divider. Each time its input is made low the count at outputs A–D advances one step. The output is in binary form. To decode this we employ the 7442 BCD-to-decimal decoder. As successive pulses are fed to the input of the 7490, the out-puts 0 to 9 of the 7442 go high in turn. A ten-stage sequence is likely to be as long as most projects will require, for it is generally inconvenient to have to step through half-a-dozen or more stages quickly to get from one function to another. For sequences between 4 and 10 stages long we can use the 7490 or other dividers, as listed opposite.

The 5-stage sequence simply uses the last three flip-flops of the divide-by-ten chain, the connection from output A to input BCD being omitted. The outputs taken from pins 9, 8, 11 (least significant binary digit first) are fed to pins 15, 14 and 13 of the decoder. Pin 12 of the decoder is grounded.

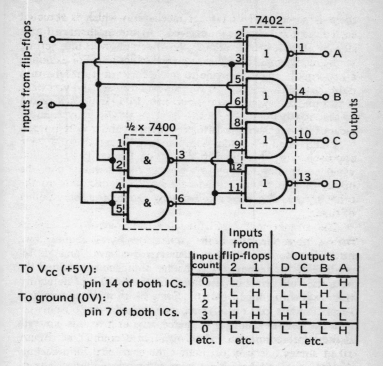

		Inputs from flip-flops		Outputs			
	Input count	2	1	D	C	B	A
	0	L	L	L	L	L	H
	1	L	H	L	L	H	L
	2	H	L	L	H	L	L
	3	H	H	H	L	L	L
	0 etc.	L etc.	L	L etc.	L	L	H

To V$_{CC}$ (+5V):
    pin 14 of both ICs.
To ground (0V):
    pin 7 of both ICs.

Fig. 10.10 Decoder to activate 1 of 4 outputs in sequence.

No. stages in seq.	Divider i.c. used	Input to pin	Join pins	NAND outputs from pins	Output from pins
5	7490	1	—	—	−11, 8, 9
6	7492	14	1−12	—	− 9, 11, 12
7	7490	14	1−12	8, 9, 12	− 8, 9, 12
8	7493	1	—	—	−11, 8, 9
9	7490	14	1−12	11, 12	11, 8, 9, 12

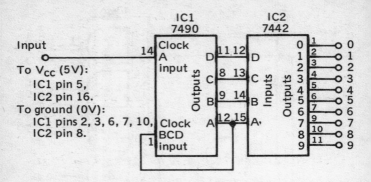

Fig. 10.11 10– stage sequential controller and decoder.

The 6-stage sequence uses the 7492 divide-by-12 counter, but not its D output. Again the outputs are taken to pins 15, 14 and 13 of the decoder. The 7-stage sequence is obtained by using the full divide-by-ten range of the 7490, but detecting when it gets to count 7 by connecting three of its outputs to a 3-input NAND gate (7410). At count 7, all three outputs go high; the NAND gate output therefore goes low; this is wired to the 'reset-0' inputs of the 7490 (pins 2 and 3), which are *not* grounded. The effect is that the counter is immediately reset to zero and begins counting again from there. The 9-stage sequence is obtained in a similar way. The 8-stage sequence uses the last three flip-flops of the 7493 divide-by-16 i.c. In this, as well as in the 5-stage circuit, the first flip-flop of the chain is unused, and is available for other purposes if required.

A CMOS version of the above circuits is much simpler to wire up (Fig. 10.12) since the divider and decoder are combined in a single i.c. This can be reset at any desired stage by using a set–reset flip-flop constructed from a 4001 i.c. (Fig. 10.13). The connections to IC2 are taken from output 0 and from *one* of outputs 1 to 9, depending on when resetting is to occur.

The two main features of the circuits described so far in this section (Figs 10.8 to 10.13) are:

148

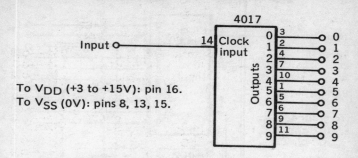

Fig. 10.12 A CMOS version of the circuit of Fig. 10.11.

(1) They have a number of outputs, only one of which goes high at any given stage. They are thus suited for controlling a sequence of functions to operate *one* at a time.

(2) The outputs may be used to drive any of the on/off switching circuits of Figures 10.1 to 10.7.

Sequential control can also be used to produce an analogue output. The stepping analogue output provided by the PPM decoder has already been described. If you have a single device that needs to be controlled in this way and no other control function is required, it is probably uneconomic to build a complete PPM system just for this purpose. An exception may be where the environment is noisy and the error-checking features of the PPM system are of particular value.

In the sequential systems of Figures 10.9 to 10.13, the controlled device performs each function in turn as it is stepped on, even though any steps being by-passed are of extremely short duration. An alternative approach to sequential control is shown in Figure 10.14. The circuit controls a set of up to 10 functions. Each function can be switched on or off independently of the others *in any order*. The outputs are used to switch low-current devices such as reed relays directly, or they can be connected to any of the on/off switching circuits of Figures 10.1 to 10.7.

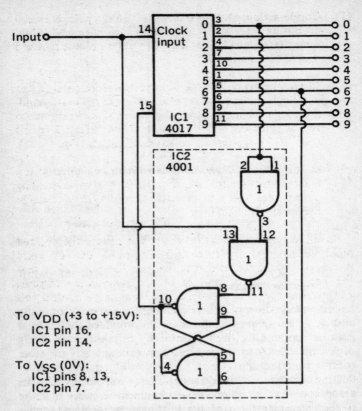

Fig. 10.13 A CMOS counter–decoder connected to reset at the 7th count, making a 6–stage sequence controller.

The principle of this method of control is that the circuit repeatedly steps through 10 stages, numbered 0 to 9. The stage number is displayed on a 7-segment LED, visible to the operator. The number changes about once every 2 seconds. To select a particular function the operator watches the changing number on the display until the required number is seen. The operator then presses the button on the hand-held transmitter. Three types of switching action are possible:

150

(1)   Toggle action: Output 0 is made high if a pulse is received during stage 0. It then stays high during all subsequent stages, including stage 0, until a pulse is received during a later stage 0.

(2)   Instantaneous pulse: If a pulse arrives during stages 1 to 3, a single instantaneous pulse appears at the corresponding output. These outputs have several applications: to switch functions on for a short period; trigger a circuit (Fig. 10.7); to step on an analogue circuit (Fig. 10.14).

(3)   On/off action of one out of a given set of outputs: If a pulse arrives during stages 4 to 9, the corresponding output goes high. At the same time all other outputs in the group 4 to 9 go low.

In all three methods, the long pulse causes the decimal point LED of the display to light, indicating that the command has been received and is being acted upon. Note that the 7-segment display must be of the *common anode* type.

Only a single-pulse transmitter is required to control this circuit. Since the circuit is triggered by the *arrival* of a pulse and its action does not depend on the length of the pulse, it may be operated by the high-intensity infra-red flash circuit of Figure 7.3. Any other single-pulse system may be used, including ultra-sonic and radio.

The logic of this circuit is explained in detail, so that the reader is able to modify its construction if necessary to adapt it to requirements. Stepping is caused by a clock circuit, based on IC1. This oscillates at about 0.6Hz. Its output is taken to a decade counter, IC3, which therefore changes stage about once every 2 seconds. The outputs are taken to a binary-to-7-segment coder (IC4), which causes the corresponding numeral to be displayed.

The input to the logic circuit is normally low, and the circuit operates on receiving a high pulse from the receiver. If the system is such that the receiver output is normally high, omit the INVERT gate. When the input pulse arrives, it triggers off the two pulse generators of IC2. These

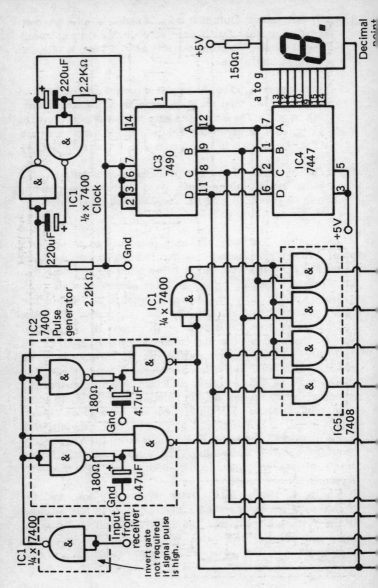

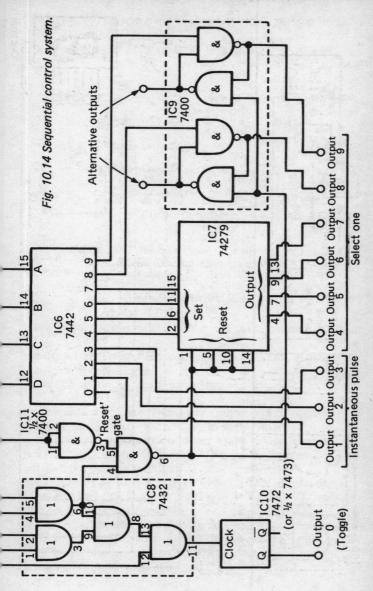

Fig. 10.14 Sequential control system.

Pins	1	2	3	4	5	6	7	8	9	10	11	12	13	14	15	16	
IC1							O							5	-	-	
IC2							O							5	-	-	
IC3		O	O		5	0	0		O						-	-	
IC4			5	5			O									5	
IC5							O							5	-	-	
IC6								O								5	
IC7			⑤					O			⑤					5	
IC8							O							5	-	-	
IC9							O							5	-	-	
IC10		⑤	⑤	⑤	⑤		O		⑤	⑤	⑤		⑤	5	-	-	(7472)
IC10		⑤	⑤	⑤	5		⑤	⑤			⑤	0		⑤	-	-	(7473)
IC11							O							5	-	-	

⑤ = connect to +5V through 1KΩ resistor.
Also connect *unused* inputs
of IC1 and IC11 in this way.

Fig. 10.14 (continued)

produce a short pulse and a long pulse; both are low-going
pulses.

The long and short pulses now take over control of the
circuit. The way they do this is described separately for
the three types of control, since their action is different:

(1) Toggle action output: The flip-flop action is obtained by
using a J-K flip-flop i.c., a 7472. If you are designing for
an application which needs a second flip-flop, it is more
economical to use a 7473 dual J-K flip-flop i.c. IC3 has
four output lines, A to D, representing the stage of the
circuit in binary code. At stage 0 all four outputs are
low (0000). The four outputs are fed to two OR gates
in IC8 (pins 1, 2, 4 and 5). When these are low the gate
outputs at pins 3 and 6 are low, so the output at pin 8 is
low. Only when all four outputs are low and the long
pulse is operative (low), does the output from IC8,
pin 11, to the clock input of IC10 go low. A low-going

154

clock input causes the Q and Q̄ outputs to change state. You can use either or both of these outputs for switching. When the circuit is next triggered in this way, Q and Q̄ change state again, so producing the toggle action.

(2) Instantaneous pulse: At each stage, the corresponding output of IC6 goes high for the duration of the long pulse. The figure shows 3 of these outputs being used directly to provide an instaneous pulse. If a normally high output and low instantaneous pulse is required, the output is inverted by passing it to one of the spare gates of IC11. The output is connected to both inputs of the NAND gate; the output from this gate is the INVERT of the input.

(3) On/off action of one of a set of outputs: The outputs from IC6 are fed to the 'set' inputs of 6 bistable gates. These can be constructed from two NAND gates, as shown in the figure, or an i.c. such as the 74279 used, which contains four bistables ready-wired. The reset inputs of all the bistables are wired together. The principle of action is that, when the circuit is triggered during any of the stages 4 to 9, all bistables are reset by the short pulse. The long pulse remains low for a period after the short pulse has finished, so the selected flip-flop is set. However, we must ensure that the relays can not be reset during stages 0 to 3, when toggle-action and instantaneous pulse action are selected. The circuit must be able to distinguish between stages 0 to 3 and stages 4 to 9. Binary numbers 0 to 3, all have zeroes as the first two digits, whereas numbers 4 to 9 have at least one '1' in the first two digits. We take the C and D outputs from IC3 and OR these together. This has already been done in IC8 for the toggle-switch circuit, so we make an additional connection to the output at pin 6. This output is low only during stages 0 to 3. The short pulse, which is a low-going pulse is inverted by one of the NAND gates of IC11. The resultant high pulse from this gate is fed to a second NAND gate, which we call the

'reset' gate. There it is NANDed with the output from the OR gate of IC8. When C and D are both low, the input to pin 4 of the 'reset' gate is low, and the short pulse can have no effect on the output of the 'reset' gate. The output of this gate remains high. The result is that the bistables can not be reset during stages 0 to 3. But, when either C or D are high (stages 4 to 9), pin 4 of the 'reset' gate is high and the high short pulse produces a short low pulse at the output of the 'reset' gate. This resets all the bistables.

The long pulse continues until after the short pulse has ended. In IC5 the long pulse is ANDed with each of the outputs from IC3. The binary code of the stage appears on the outputs of IC5 for the duration of the long pulse. This causes the selected outputs of IC6 to go high for the same period. After the reset action of the short pulse is completed, *one* of the bistables remains set. If you require a state in which *none* of the outputs are set, one of the outputs must be sacrificed. Thus, if output 4 is chosen as the 'none set' output selecting stages 5 to 9 makes *one* of the outputs 5 to 9 go high. Selecting 4 makes *all* of outputs 5 to 9 go low.

The description above outlines the main points of design in this circuit. Other combinations of the three types of switching can be implemented by suitable decoding of the output of IC3.

Multiple-pulse control

In 4-digit systems, the decoder has 4 output terminals, any one or more of which can be high at any given time. It is possible to use these outputs directly to control 4 separate functions independently. They can be used to control transistor switches and relays, as described earlier in this chapter. The problem is to work out which binary number must be transmitted in order to bring a given combination of devices into action. One way to do this is use a specially designed transmitter keyboard. Figure 10.15 shows a 4-key keyboard (with a fifth 'transmit' key) for connection to the coder of Figure 6.4. To operate this, press the key of each device that is to be

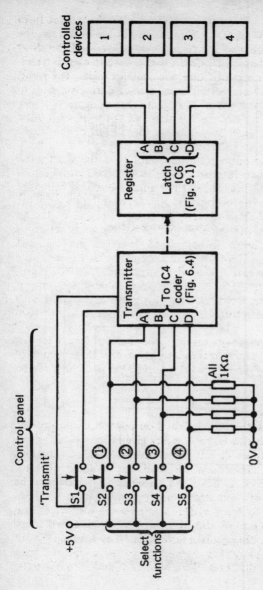

Fig. 10.15 Controlling 4 devices independently.

157

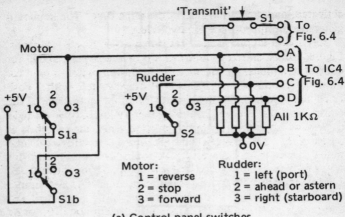

(a) Control panel-switches.

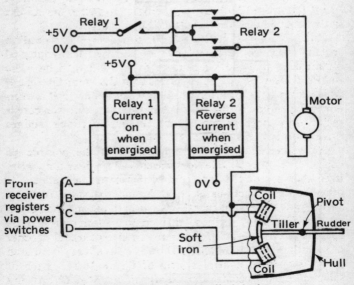

(b) Connections to controlled devices.

Fig. 10.16 Controlling a model boat.

158

activated, and press 'transmit' at the same time. The keyboard generates the appropriate binary code.

Keyboard layout is not restricted to a row of buttons. Figure 10.16a shows a modification of the scheme above for control of a model motor boat. A 3-position switch is used for motor direction control. This is a rotary switch, with 3 positions and 2 wafers. Preferably it is mounted on the side of the control console. Instead of the customary knob, it would have a lever which is in the vertical position when the switch is at position 2. The lever is pushed forward for 'forward' and pulled backward for 'reverse'. A rotary switch wired in this way produces 3 binary codes: 00 for stop, 01 for forward and 11 for reverse. The least significant digit (A) determines whether the motor is running or not. The next digit (B) determines its direction. There is no need for code 10, for its effect is identical to code 00. Figure 10.16b shows how the motor is controlled by two relays, one to switch the motor on or off (controlled by digit A), the other to switch the current in the required direction (controlled by digit B).

Rudder control in Figure 10.16 employs a 3-position switch, which could be a centre-biassed switch (Chapter 5) mounted so that the lever moves to left and to right. The rudder is held by two light springs (not shown in the figure) which keep it in a central position when neither coil is energised. When one of the coils is energised, the soft-iron core is pulled into the coil, turning the rudder. Steering requires three codes in digits C and D: 00, 01, 10.

Altogether, the above system uses 9 of the possible 16 codes. The other 7 codes are 'wasted'. This does not matter if all that is required is to control the motor and rudder. If other control functions, such as 'sound the siren' or 'drop anchor' are to be implemented, we need to expand the system by *decoding* the 4 digits so that up to 16 functions may be controlled. Figure 10.17 illustrates a range of useful decoder i.c.s, both in TTL and CMOS. The 7442 has already been used in the sequential control system of Figure 10.14. Each of these decoders accepts four binary inputs A to D. At any given time the output corresponding to the binary input goes high, while all other outputs go low. The 7442 only allows input in the range 0 to 9, as does its CMOS counterpart, the

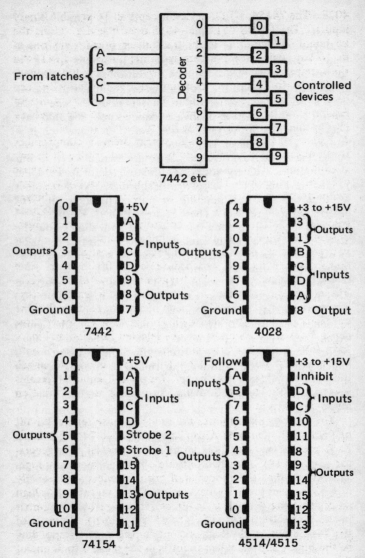

Fig. 10.17 Decoder IC's.

160

4028. The 74154, a TTL device, accepts all 16 possible binary inputs. The CMOS 4514 and 4515 does likewise. Using the keyboard of Figure 5.4 in the transmitter, pressing any one of its 16 keys will cause the corresponding output of a 74154 in the receiver to go high. Though decoders allow independent control of 16 functions, their limitation is that *only one* can be high at any one time. By contrast, the four outputs of Figure 10.15 are independently controlled and *any combination* of them can be high at any one time.

Figure 10.18 shows a circuit which offers a compromise. It allows up to 8 functions to be switched on or off, in any combination. The transmitter is based on the multiple pulse coder of Figure 6.4. The input interface has an 8-way rotary switch to select which function is to be controlled. A binary switch could be used in place of this, output D (MSD) not being used. The remaining controls consist of two push-buttons or switches. S2 is a double-pole button (i.e. it has two entirely separate pairs of contacts). It is called the 'on' button as it is used to switch the selected function on. One pair of contacts replaces the 'transmit' button of Figure 6.4. The other pair are wired as shown so that, when the button is pressed, input D of IC4 is made high. The result is that the code group transmitted has digit D high, and the lower three digits represent the number of the selected function, in binary form. S3 is another 'transmit' button, wired in parallel with the 'transmit' contacts of S2. This button is used to switch the selected function off. When S3 is pressed, input D remains low, while the lower 3 digits correspond to the function number, as before.

The receiver incorporates the multiple-pulse register circuit of Figure 9.1. Outputs A to C are fed to two 7442 decoders. Each decoder receives its D input from a special pulse generator (Fig. 10.19). The two outputs of this are normally high. This means that the D inputs of both decoders are normally high. Whatever the levels of A, B and C, the fact that D is high means that the decoder is, in effect, receiving a binary number in the range 1000 to 1111 (8 to 15 in decimal). Outputs of the 7442 are normally high, except for the one corresponding to the binary input. When input is in the range 0 to 7, one of the outputs 0 to 7 is low and the rest are high. When the input

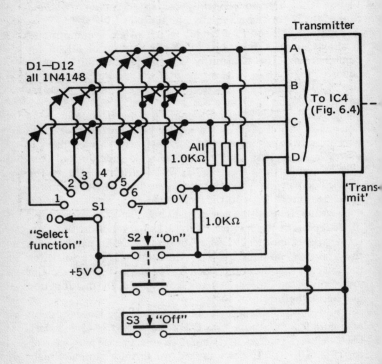

Fig. 10.18 Controlling 8 devices independently.

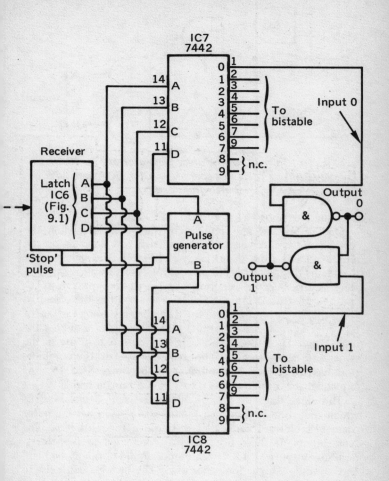

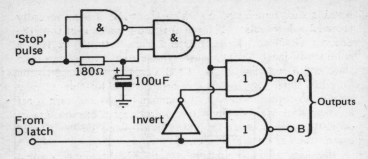

Fig. 10.19 Details of the pulse generator of Fig. 10.18. The INVERT gate can be a spare NAND or NOR gate with its inputs wired together.

is in the range 8 to 15, all outputs 0 to 7 are high.

One output of the pulse generator goes low when the 'stop' pulse is received. Which one goes low depends on the input received from the D latch of IC6. If D is high, output B remains high, but output A goes low. The result is that IC7 receives the selected function number at its inputs A to C, and a low at its D input. The combination has the effect of a number in the range 0 to 7. The corresponding output of IC7 goes low, all other outputs remaining high. At the same time, input D of IC8 remains high. Inputs A to C are in the same state as those of IC7 but, since D is high, the combination has the effect of a number in the range 8 to 15. As explained above, all outputs 0 to 7 of IC8 remain high.

The final stage of this circuit consists of 8 bistables, of which only one is shown in Figure 10.18. The set inputs of these bistables are connected to outputs 0 to 7 of IC7. The reset inputs of these bistables are connected to the corresponding outputs of IC8. Both inputs should normally be high. One output is high, the other low. The bistable can exist in either one of two stable states. If a low pulse is applied to input 0, output 0 changes from low to high (unless it is already high) and output 1 changes from high to low (unless already low). Further low pulses on input 0 have no effect, but a low pulse on input 1 causes output 1 to go high, and output 0 to go low. Further pulses on input 1 have no effect. Thus the

164

bistable can 'remember' on which input line it most recently received a low pulse. If input 0 is fed from output 0 of the decoder (IC7) and input 1 is fed from output 0 of IC8, a command signal '0000' causes the bistable to assume one state and a command signal '1000' causes it to change to the opposite state. By setting and resetting the bistable we may arrange to turn a motor on at command 0000 and turn it off at command 1000. Since the outputs of a bistable are of opposite sense, a single bistable can turn one device off and switch another on simultaneously.

The state of the D digit determines whether the controlled function is turned on or off. The state of this digit depends on whether the operator presses the 'on' or 'off' button of the transmitter after selecting the function. Each bistable is independently controlled, so that setting or resetting one has no effect on the others. One or more functions may therefore be switched on in any combination.

Figure 10.20 illustrates a circuit based on the same principles as that of Figure 10.18, but providing for analogue control plus on—off control for 3 functions. Instead of the 7442 decoders there are 7475 latches. The output from the pulse generator triggers either IC7 (analogue) or IC8 (on—off) to register the state of digits A to C, depending on whether D is high or low. The transmitter has an 8-way rotary switch (or binary switch) to select speed. The code produced by the switch is transmitted when the 'transmit speed' button is pressed. To control the functions, one or more of the 'select functions' buttons is pressed and held; then the 'transmit functions' button is pressed. A suitable circuit for the analogue control is shown in Figure 10.21, and is described in the next paragraph. If this circuit is used in conjunction with Figure 10.20, simply omit the D connections (to pins 2 and 3 of IC1).

The multiple-pulse transmitter produces a 4-digit binary number. The code is transmitted and eventually appears in the latch registers of the receiver. The next step is to convert this digital representation of speed into an analogue form. The circuit for doing this, a digital-to-analogue converter, is shown in Figure 10.21. It uses a CMOS i.c. because current from the outputs can be summed simply by feeding them through

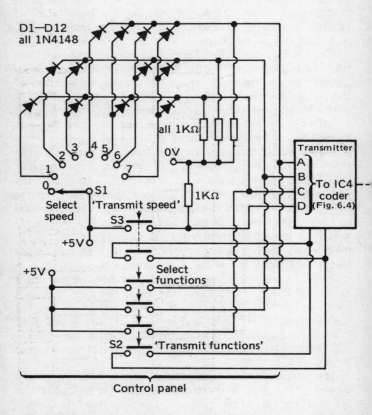

Fig. 10.20 Controlling 4 devices, one with analogue control.

166

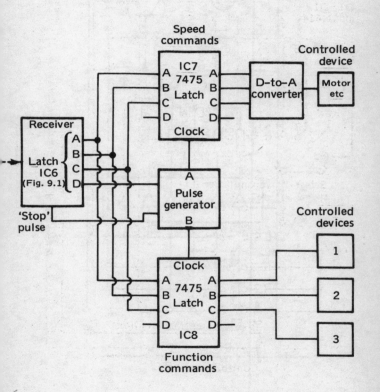

167

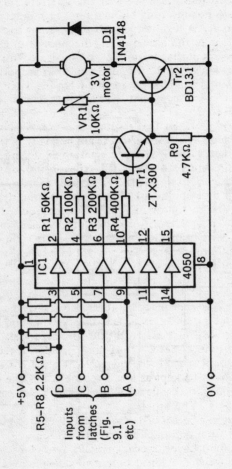

Fig. 10.21 Digital-to-Analogue converter.

resistors to the base of TR1. This does not work with TTL. Because we are taking outputs from TTL (the latch of the decoder circuit) and using these as inputs to CMOS we need the pull-up resistors R5—R8 at the interface. The 4050 i.c. contains 6 non-inverting buffers; for a high input, each gives a high output. A high output causes a current to flow through the resistor to the base of TR1, the amount of current being inversely proportional to the resistance. With the values shown in Figure 10.21 the total current is proportional to the 4-digit binary number represented by the latch outputs, D being the most significant digit. Resistors with values 50kΩ and 400kΩ are not available in the standard series, but can be made up by joining two resistors in series. In practice, resistors of values 47kΩ and 390kΩ are normally close enough to the required values. TR1 is connected as an emitter-follower, and so the potential across R9 varies in proportional to the total base current of TR1. The variable resistor VR1 supplies sufficient base current to TR2 to keep the transistor switched on, and the motor running at its lowest required speed even when all latches are zero. In any other condition, additional current flows from TR1, turning TR2 more fully on and thus increasing motor speed. The amount of increase is proportional to the binary number stored in the latch. VR1 can be replaced by a fixed resistor if the same minimum speed is always required.

As well as controlling motor speed it may be required to control motor direction. The simplest method is to use a relay (Fig. 10.22), controlled through a separate channel from that controlling speed. It is then possible to control both direction and speed independently. If space is restricted and weight has to be kept as low as possible, use one of the d.i.l. relays with two double-throw contacts. These can be driven directly by a TTL output.

The system described above allows one to change speed *instantly* from one value to another. Often it is sufficient to increase or decrease speed *gradually* until the required new speed is reached. Since only two commands are required ('increase speed', 'decrease speed') instead of a distinct command for each of the possible values of speed, we are able to effect a considerable economy in the transmission of

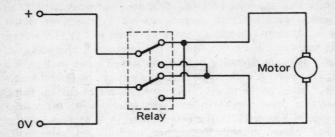

*Fig. 10.22 Using a double-pole double-throw relay
as a reversing switch.*

instructions and can use these savings to provide for instructions of other kinds. Figure 10.23 shows how this function may be added to the digital-to-analogue converter of Figure 10.21. The 74193 is a counter that may be clocked to count either up or down from its initial state. A low pulse to pin 5 causes it to increase its count by 1. This takes effect as the input rises from low to high. Count 15 is followed by count 0 when counting up; count 0 is followed by count 15 when counting down. By using this i.c., speed can be controlled over the whole range of the D-to-A converter by using only two lines. The remaining two lines can be used in various ways. Figure 10.23 indicates one possibility. Line C is used to clear the counter by delivering a high pulse, so immediately reducing speed to zero, or to whatever minimum speed has been decided upon. Line D can be used to operate a flip-flop so that the direction of the motor can be reversed by toggle action. On four lines we have complete control of speed and direction, with instantaneous 'stop'. It is also possible to load a pre-set value into the counter. The input pins (see Fig. A.2g, Appendix A) can be individually wired either to ground or to +5V so that, when the 'load' input is made low, a predetermined value appears at the outputs of the i.c.

If the 'clear' function shown in Figure 10.23 is not required, this input must be grounded.

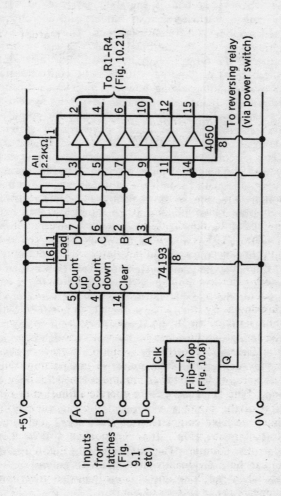

Fig. 10.23 Circuit for producing stepped increase or decrease of analogue values.

171

Positional control

Ratchet mechanisms are available, or can be constructed, that operate whenever a coil is energised and can be used for moving control surfaces such as rudders and ailerons into a restricted number of different positions. These require only a power transistor to operate them and can be easily controlled by circuits of the types already described. For finer control a servo-mechanism is required. In this the control surface is moved by reduction-gearing powered by a small motor, the surface usually being connected to the gear system by a flexible cable. The gear system also turns the spindle of a variable resistor. In the digital proportional system the variable resistor is wired as part of a pulse generator, and there is a circuit to compare the length of pulse generated locally with the length of pulse received from the transmitter. If they are unequal in length the motor is made to run in the appropriate direction so as to turn the variable resistor and adjust the length of the locally-generated pulse to make it closer in length to the received pulse. When the two pulses match exactly, the motor is stopped, having moved the control surface to the required position.

The digital-to-analogue system operates in a similar way, but instead of matching pulse lengths, we match a current produced by the variable resistor against a current produced by the digital-to-analogue converter. A circuit for doing this is shown in Figure 10.24. The converter output comes from 4 resistors, shown with standard values here, though it could also function with only 3 buffers in action if a 3-digit code is being used. The currents from the converter and from the wiper of the variable resistor VR1 are compared by the operational amplifier. This is a CMOS i.c., so the usual precautions should be taken when handling it (page 28). This type is chosen because it can work on a low supply voltage and its output swings strongly toward either supply rail. It is half-way between the two rails (= +2.5V) when the two currents are equal, but falls sharply to 0V when the current from the variable resistors is very slightly less than that from the converter. The output from the operational amplifier goes to two pairs of transistors. These are connected as a pair of Schmitt triggers, so that though they may be turned on by an increase

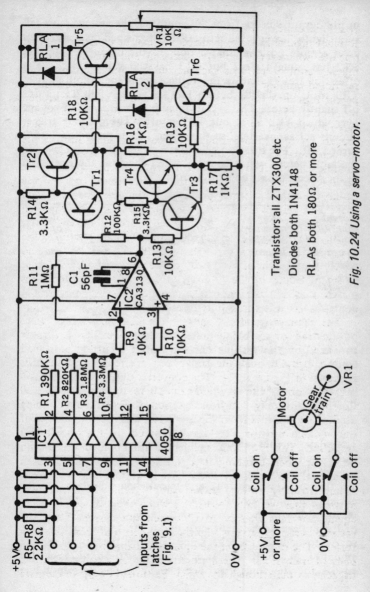

Transistors all ZTX300 etc
Diodes both 1N4148
RLAs both 180Ω or more

Fig. 10.24 Using a servo-motor.

173

in the output voltage from the amplifier, the voltage must fall to a slightly lower level before they are turned on again. This gives a more positive 'snap-action' to the circuit. Note that R12 has value 100kΩ but R13 has the value 10kΩ. The effect of this is that as the voltage from the amplifier rises TR3 turns on slightly before TR1; as voltage falls TR1 turns off slightly before TR3. Thus there is a small range of voltage over which TR3 is on but TR1 is off. The Schmitt trigger circuits act as inverters, so that when TR1 is turned on TR5 is turned off. The three possible states of the circuit are given in the table below, which is useful when checking the operation of the circuit during construction:

Current from VR1 wiper, compared with that from d-to-a converter	Output of operational amplifier (approx.)	State of TR1	State of TR3	State of TR5 and RLA1 coil	State of TR6 and RLA2 coil
higher	more than 2.8V	on	on	off	off
approx. equal	2.4–2.8V	on	off	off	on
lower	less than 2.4V	off	off	on	on

The relay switches can be arranged so that the motor turns one way when the wiper current is greater than the converter current, turns in the opposite direction when wiper current is less than converter current, and is switched off when the two currents are more-or-less equal. By making the connections to the motor of the correct polarity, the direction of turning of the motor can be made such that it turns the wiper of VR1 so as to reduce the difference between the inputs to the amplifier. As the difference approaches zero the motor is switched off and the control surface remains in the corresponding

174

fixed position, until a new command signal is received and the process of finding the balance-point is repeated to obtain a new position of the control surface.

With 8-digit multiple-pulse control, 8 devices may be controlled independently by extending the principle of the circuit in Figure 10.15. The circuits of Figures 10.18 and 10.20 may similarly be adapted to 8-digit operation. However, the greatest benefit of doubling the number of digits is realized in analogue control systems. With 8 digits, the digital equivalent of the analogue quantity ranges from 0 to its maximum value in 256 steps. The difference between adjacent steps are so small that control is almost indistinguishable from true analogue.

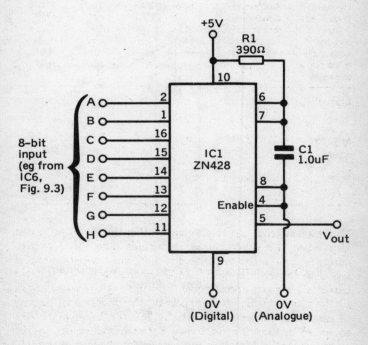

Fig. 10.25 8–digit digital–to–analogue converter.

175

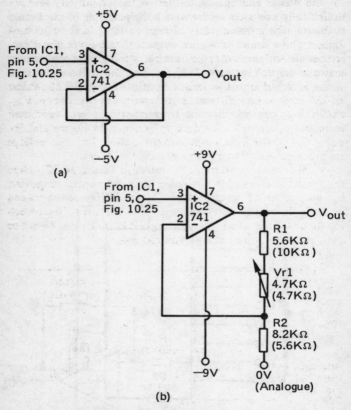

Fig. 10.26 Buffers for the D-to-A converter output:
(a) voltage follower;
(b) output amplifier for doubling
(or trebling) the voltage range.

Figure 10.25 is the circuit for an 8-digit D-to-A converter. Its output voltage ranges from 0V to 2.5V as the digital input ranges from zero to 255. Separate ground pins are provided for the digital and analogue sides of the circuit, if these are individually powered. Otherwise both pins may be connected to a common ground. Only a small current, in the region of 1mA may be drawn from the output. Normally a larger current will be required, and possibly it will be necessary to increase the voltage range. If so, the output from the converter is fed to an operational amplifier. Figure 10.26a shows an op amp wired as a voltage follower. In this circuit V_{out} equals V_{in}, but the amount of current that may be drawn from the op amp is considerably greater. In Figure 10.26b, not only is the maximum current greater but the voltage range is doubled (0 to 5V) or trebled (0 to 7.5V).

Another output interface is shown in Figure 10.27. Here the operational amplifier is wired as a differential amplifier, its output being proportional to the difference between currents flowing to its two inputs. The current to the inverting input is controlled by adjusting VR1, which can be set so as to give zero output at any required level.

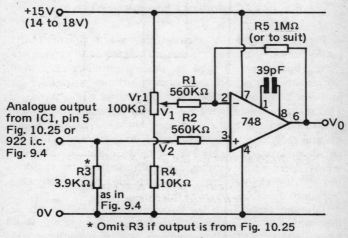

Fig. 10.27 An interface for the analogue outputs.

The maximum rating of most operational amplifiers is 500mW which is less than most low-voltage motors work at when running under load. A rating between 1W and 6W is common.

It is therefore necessary to drive the motor by using a power transistor. Figure 10.28 shows a straightforward way of doing this; this method can also be used for brightness control of lamps and other applications.

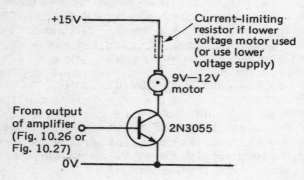

Fig. 10.28 Controlling a low-voltage d.c. motor.

Figure 10.29 shows a circuit for motor control that is particularly useful when the motor is subjected to varying load during operation. If load on the motor increases, current through the motor increases, causing a rise in potential at the junction between the motor and the emitter of the transistor. This rising potential is fed to the inverting input of the amplifier, causing its output to fall, switching the transistor slightly off and reducing the flow of current to the motor. Thus, this circuit maintains a steady current to the motor, keeping it at steady speed under varying load. It also allows the motor to run steadily at low speed, without jerking, and gives greater realism to models powered in this way.

In audio applications the analogue outputs can be used for the control of volume. With three analogue outputs it would be possible to control two channels of a stereophonic system independently, and use the third output for balance control.

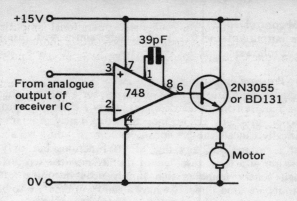

Fig. 10.29 Stabilised speed control for a d.c. motor.

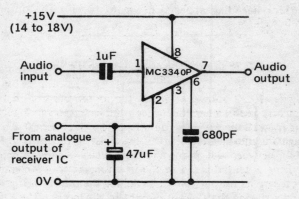

*Fig. 10.30 Controlling volume levels
in audio remote control applications.*

A device for controlling volume is the MC3340P electronic
attenuator (Fig. 10.30). By varying the current supplied to
its control pin (pin 2), the audio signal may be attenuated in
the range 0 to 90dB.

PPM control

The outputs of the 922 PPM decoder and ways to use them are as follows:

(1) *Program outputs:*

These outputs are intended primarily for switching channels on a remote control television set. Only 1 channel or program is to be on at any given time. Selecting a new program automatically cancels the previous selection. If you have a model that is to perform any one of 10 functions but only one function at a time, the logic of the i.c. provides ten different 4digit binary numbers that simply need decoding. If the outputs are used direct, we have a run from binary 6 to binary 15 (see table on page 132) and the obvious choice for a decoder is the CMOS 4514 or 4515 i.c. These are binary to 1-of-16 decoders, the 4514 giving a high output on the selected output line and the 4515 giving a low output on the selected lines, all other lines having the reverse state. A circuit for decoding appears in Figure 10.31. The outputs

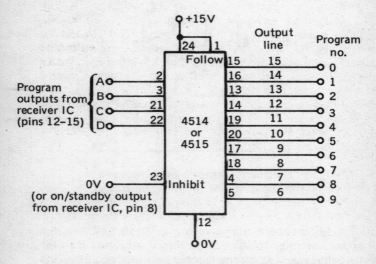

Fig. 10.31 Decoding program outputs from PPM IC's.

on output lines 6 to 15 may then be used to drive lamps, motors, relays and other devices as described already. Remember to leave one code free as an 'all-off' code should you want to have the state in which no functions are in operation. Another way of doing this is to connect 'standby' output to the 'inhibit' input of the 4514 or 4515. This is initially high, so the initial program output (1111) is inhibited. As soon as a program command is received 'standby' output goes low, allowing the decoder to produce the appropriate output. On pressing 'standby' the 'standby' output goes high again, thus inhibiting the output from the decoder and causing all functions to cease.

If 4 or fewer functions are to be controlled by program outputs, a decoder is unnecessary. Each function is controlled by one of the program outputs A, B, C and D. Using invert gates if necessary, the functions are brought into action when the corresponding line goes low. Thus we can command program 1 to make line D go low, program 2 to make line C go low; program 4 to make line B go low; and program 8 to make line A go low. These lines could instead be connected to two flip-flops giving toggle action on two functions (Fig. 10.32). Program 8 provides on—off control for one function; program 4 provides on—off for the other function. These are but a few examples of the ways the program outputs can be used. In any given circumstance it is generally a simple matter to devise the required logic, based on the principles discussed here and elsewhere in the book.

The way of using the outputs of the 926/929 range of receiver i.c.s is the same as described above for the program outputs of the 922. They can also be used to drive switching transistors as in Figures 10.1 to 10.4.

(2)   *Analogue outputs:*
Each of these may be used in the same way as the outputs from the D-to-A converter of Figure 10.25. The maximum output current from each output is 1.3mA. If the sink resistors have the value 3.9k as shown in Figure 9.4, the potential at each output can be varied from zero to 5V. With resistors of greater values, higher potentials can be obtained

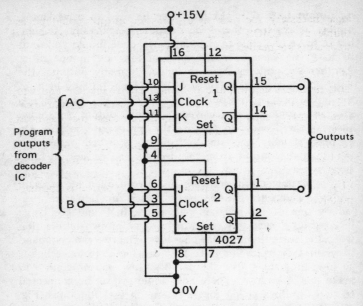

Fig. 10.32 Producing a toggle action on program outputs. Inverse action is obtained by connections to pins 2 and 14.

but there is loss of linearity. Figures 10.26 to 10.30 illustrate various ways of using the analogue outputs.

(3) *On/Standby output:*
This is initially high, goes low whenever a program change is commanded and may be made high by 'standby' command. It then remains high until another program change is commanded. This could be used to control a muting operation in an audio application. The sound would be muted by the 'standby' command, and restored whenever a new program was selected. In model control it could be used to switch off power to several sections simultaneously pending the activation of one or more sections by program outputs. In other words — a true 'standby' control, putting the model temporarily in an inactive condition while awaiting fresh instructions. The

logic necessary for making use of this output could be as simple as a CMOS buffer gate, controlling whatever power transistors are needed to effect the required actions.

(4) *Pulse output:*

This produces a low pulse of length approximately equal to $1/f_{osc}$ whenever any command signal is received. One application of this is some visual indication that the signal has been received. This could take the form of an LED which flashes to indicate that event. Figure 10.33 shows how a 555 timer i.c. can be triggered to flash an LED once on receipt of a pulse from Pulse Output. The length of flash depends on the values of C1 and R1. With the values given the period is approximately 2 seconds.

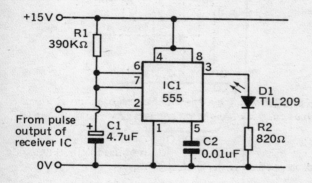

Fig. 10.33 Using the pulse output to give indication that a signal has been received.

(5) *Toggle output:*

This output is low at switch-on. If 'Analogue 2' output is reduced to zero, 'Toggle' output goes high. It remains high for as long as 'Analogue 2' output is zero; if 'Analogue 2' output is increased, either by using the 'Analogue 2+' command or by the 'Normalise' command, 'Toggle' output returns to low. When 'Analogue 2' output is greater than zero, 'Toggle' output can be made high by sending 'Toggle' command. It can then be made low again by sending any program command, any analogue command, 'Standby' or 'Normalise'. The change from high to low occurs immediately *after* the command has been effected.

Controlling a computer

As in Chapter 5, we deal with the popular computers individually.

Amstrad CPC 464, 664 and 6128. The easiest way of sending signals to the Amstrad computers is by way of the joystick port (Fig. 10.34). Use a D-type 9-way *socket*, connecting the ground of the receiver circuit to the 'ground' pin of the socket and the data line from the receiver to pin D0 of the socket. The joystick port accepts only TTL inputs (maximum input voltage is +5V).

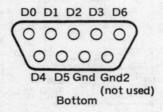

Top

D0 D1 D2 D3 D6

D4 D5 Gnd Gnd2
(not used)

Bottom

Fig. 10.34 The joystick connector in Amstrad computers, as seen from the rear of the machine.

The state of the input is then read by using a statement such as:

$$X = JOY(0)$$

If D0 is high, the statement returns the value X=0. If D0 is low, then X=1. By suitable programming it is possible for the computer to analyse an incoming chain of pulses received at D0. In effect, the program takes the place of a 4-digit or 8-digit decoder.

If your receiver includes a multiple-pulse decoder with a 4-digit or 8-digit output, lines A to D (or G) may be connected to D0 to D3 (or D6) of the joystick. There is no pin for D7, so only 7-digit input is accepted. When using 4-digit input, D4 to D6 may be left unconnected and are read as if they were high. The corresponding values of JOY(0) are given in Table 10.1.

Table 10.1 Values obtained when receiving data

State of data input		Value of JOY(0)
All high	11111111	0
D0 low	11111110	1
D1 low	11111101	2
D2 low	11111011	4
D3 low	11110111	8
D4 low	11101111	16
D5 low	11011111	32
D6 low	10111111	64

If more than one data input is low, the value of JOY(0) equals the sum of the values given in the table.

BBC Microcomputer. The User Port accepts only TTL inputs (maximum voltage is +5V). The first step is to set DDRB so that some or all of the lines are inputs:

```
10 A%=&97:X%=&62:Y%=254:CALL &FFF4
```

The statements above set line D0 (Fig. 5.9) as input and the rest as outputs. For 4-digit input (D0 to D3) the value of Y% should be 240; for 8-digit input (all data lines as inputs) it should be 0.

Having done this we may read the value of data present on the line(s) as follows:

```
20 A%=&96:R=(USR(&FFF4) AND &10000)/&10000
```

The statements above return R having the value (0 or 1) on the data line D0. For 4-bit input (on D0 to D3) substitute '&F0000' for the *first* '&10000' in the statement. For 8-digit input substitute 'FF0000'.

Commodore 64. To set DDRB for input on D0 only, use:

    10 POKE 56579,254

To read the value on line D0, use

    20 R=PEEK(56577) AND 1

R has the value 0 or 1, depending on the state of the line. To read 4-digit inputs the corresponding statements are:

    10 POKE 56579,240
    20 R=PEEK(56577) AND 15

To read 8-digit input, the statements are:

    10 POKE 56579,0
    20 R=PEEK(56577)

Spectrum 48K, + and 128K. The Spectrum does not have a User Port, but an interface to the microphone (MIC) socket may be used instead. Figure 10.35 shows a simple interface for a single-digit input. The state of the input is read by using IN 61438. Unfortunately, the value obtained is somewhat erratic. With low input (0V) the value is normally 255, but is occasionally 191. With high input it is normally 191, but is occasionally 255. Thus we have to read input several times and use the total to determine the state of the input. The program below reads the input 20 times and then prints out the input state:

    10 LET x=0
    20 FOR j=1 TO 20
    30 LET x=x + IN 61438
    40 NEXT j

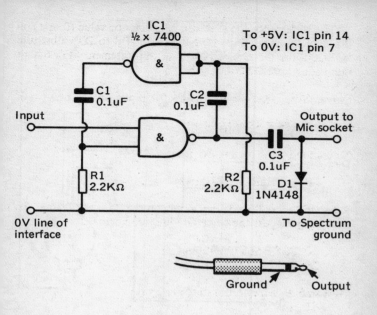

Fig. 10.35 Interfacing to the Spectrum computers.

```
50  IF x > 4800 THEN PRINT "High": GO TO 70
60  PRINT "Low"
70  PAUSE 5
80  GO TO 10
```

After experimenting with this program for a while, you should be able to adapt it for reading in a series of pulses and analysing the results. The pulse rate must be slow if reliable results are to be obtained.

Stepper motors

Stepper motors have many applications, especially in robotics, so this section includes circuits suitable for remote control of such motors. The operation of a stepper motor is best done by using a special controller i.c., the SAA1027 (Fig. 10.36).

187

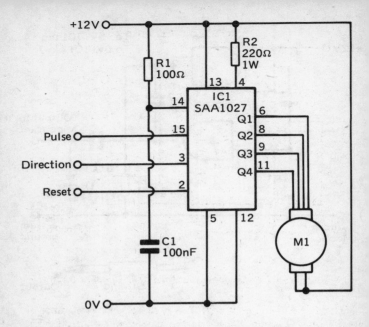

Fig. 10.36 Using an IC to control a stepper motor.

The motor rotates a step at a time whenever a high-going pulse is fed to pin 15 of the i.c. A motor may take 48 steps to perform a complete revolution. The direction of turn is controlled by the input to pin 3. If this is 0V, the motor turns in a clockwise direction. If it is 12V it turns in an anti-clockwise direction. The other control available is the reset, pin 2. This may be connected to 12V, in which case resetting is inoperative. If connected to 0V, the stepper is held reset, and the motor stops turning.

There are two aspects to stepper motor control. One is that by regulating the *rate* at which pulses are supplied, we can control the *speed* of rotation. Secondly by feeding a given *number* of pulses to the controller i.c. we can control the angle through which the spindle turns — we have control of *position*. This latter feature is of importance in controlling models and robots.

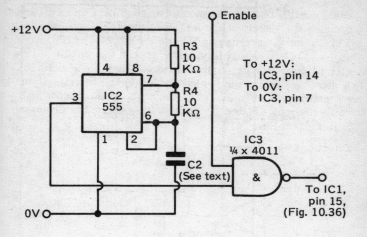

Fig. 10.37 Pulse generator for the stepper motor.

The 555 timer i.c. is useful as a pulse generator, since it works on the same voltage as the motor and controller i.c. Figure 10.37 shows the 555 wired to produce the stepping pulses. The output of the 555 can be connected directly to the pulse input of the controller. If C2 has the value 4.7μF, the pulse rate is about 100ms, so the motor takes about 5 seconds to make a complete revolution. Even slower speeds are obtainable by increasing the value of C2 or of the resistors. Increased speeds are obtained by reducing C2; if this is 0.22μF, the motor rotates about 4 times a second. This is close to the maximum speed obtainable.

If the motor is to operate at a fixed speed, and to be stopped and started by remote control, all that is needed is the AND gate of Figure 10.37 acting as an enabling gate. When the enable input is high, the motor turns. This input can be controlled by a single-pulse system, or by a single output from any other digital system. If directional control is required too, then two latches, controlled by a sequential pulse system would be the simplest solution. The 4 outputs from the multiple-pulse decoder of Figure 9.1, for example could control two stepper motors turning them on or off and deciding the direction of turn. Since the decoder is based on TTL circuitry, operating at 5V, and the stepping circuits work at 12 volts, it is essential to interface the two circuits. This may be done by using transistors as switches (e.g. Fig. 10.1b). A more convenient way, especially if there are several outputs to interface, is to use a TTL gate with open-collector high-voltage output. Figure 10.38 shows how to use one of the six buffer gates of the 7417.

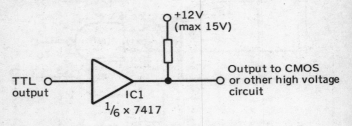

Fig. 10.38 Interfacing TTL output to CMOS or other high-voltage devices.

The circuits outlined so far depend on a pulse generator in the controlled device, operating at a constant rate. A straightforward way of controlling the pulse rate remotely would be to arrange for resistors of different values to be switched in place of R3, using relays. A more elegant solution to speed control is shown in Figure 10.39. IC1 generates pulses at a fixed rate, the fastest rate that is required. The pulses are fed to a counter (IC2), the outputs of which count round the binary sequence 0000 to 1111 once every sixteen pulses. The four outputs each go to an exclusive-OR gate of IC3. The other input to each gate comes from latches of a multiple-pulse decoder (e.g. Fig. 9.1 or the outputs of a 928 or 929 PPM receiver). These outputs are set to hold any value between 0000 and 1111. Counting proceeds until the four output levels from IC2 are identical to those from the control latches. At this instant the outputs of all four exclusive-OR

190

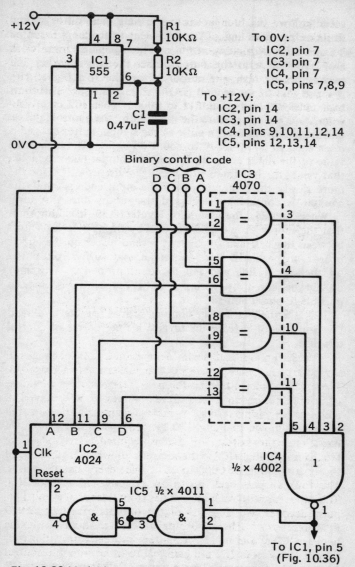

Fig. 10.39 Variable–rate pulse generator for the stepper motor.

191

gates go low. All four inputs to the NOR gate of IC4 are low so its output goes high. A pulse is sent to the stepper motor i.c. and the motor steps on once. The high pulse from IC4 is also NANDed with the output from the timer. When the two inputs are high, the output of the first NAND gate goes low and that of the second NAND gate goes high. This short high pulse resets the counter to 0000. Thus IC2 counts up from 0000 until it reaches the value set by the control latches. At this point it delivers a pulse to the stepper motor i.c. and is reset back to 0000, ready to count up again. The higher the value of the input code, the longer the counter takes to match that value, the less frequently the high pulse from IC4 and the more slowly the motor turns. If the input code is 0000, the counter is continually reset and the motor does not turn.

When building the circuit of Figure 10.39, it is important that the supply should be decoupled by wiring 0.1μ capacitors between the 12V and 0V lines at several places on the circuit board. In particular the counter i.c. may suffer from pulses on the supply line and fail to count properly. This may usually be cured by wiring a $0.1\mu F$ capacitor as close as possible to pins 7 and 14.

IC2 is actually a 7-stage counter so it is feasible to extend the principle of this circuit to give a finer degree of control of speed.

Chapter 11

GETTING STARTED

It has been assumed in earlier chapters that you already have a remote control application in mind. If so, the first thing to do is to decide which type of transmission link to employ (Chapter 2) and what methods of control to use (Chapter 4). Then Chapters 5 to 10 provide you with the circuit modules to use for building the system. However, if you have bought this book simply with the idea of exploring the possibilities of remote control, you may prefer some guidance when designing your first system. This chapter makes some suggestions for easy applications of remote control techniques. For each application, it outlines how to assemble a system from the modules already described. The suggestions are intended only as starting points. When you have built a project, or perhaps even while you are planning it, you may think of improvements to make it better suited to your needs, or to extend it in some way. The flexible approach of the book allows you the maximum freedom to modify, extend and generally to experiment with applications of remote control technology.

The projects described in this chapter are all suitable for a beginner, though some of them may interest the advanced enthusiast too. Whether you are a beginner or an expert, read through the detailed description of the first project. It contains advice and points of general importance, printed in **bold type**, that apply to most projects, simple or otherwise.

Simple on/off switching
There are many applications for switching something on and off remotely. Below we list some examples, but the reader can probably think of many more, depending upon his or her individual interests.

(1) *On/off control for a radio set or record player.* It is preferable for the radio or player to be a battery powered model. This eliminates the difficulties of having mains voltages on

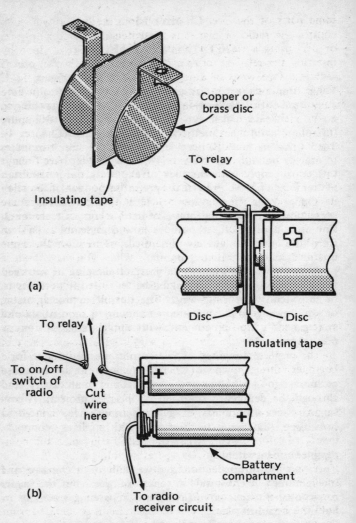

Fig. 11.1 Power–supply switching: (a) battery sandwich, 'exploded' view and section showing sandwich inserted between two cells in the battery compartment; (b) Wiring a relay in series with the on/off switch.

some parts of the circuit. The obvious method by which to control the radio or player is to switch its power supply on or off, using a remotely controlled relay. This is done by inserting the relay in series with the instrument's own on/off switch. **Two ways of doing this are shown in Figure 11.1.** These methods are applicable to other battery powered equipment too. Method (b) involves cutting or unsoldering a wire inside the instrument. If your instrument is still under the manufacturer's guarantee, **note that cutting wires or making other modifications may invalidate the guarantee.**

Many types of light-duty relay are available. Reed relays operate on low voltages so are ideal for use in conjunction with TTL or CMOS. **Check the operating voltage** of the relay in the supplier's catalogue before you order. There are advantages in using the **miniature reed relays** that are available in a casing of the same size and style as a TTL or CMOS i.c. These are conveniently mounted on the same board as the other components.

Since this is a beginner's project, **ultra-sound or infra-red** makes a good choice of transmission link. If the device is to be activated only for as long as the control button is pressed, choose a single-pulse system. Otherwise a sequential-pulse system with a flip-flop can be used to toggle a press-on/press-off action. The elements of a suggested ultra-sonic system are shown in Figure 11.2. The transmitter is built on a single board, is battery-powered (PP3) and may be housed in a case small enough for holding in the hand. Use a small plastic food or cosmetic container, buy a cheap plastic box from Woolworth's or a (more expensive!) special case for hand-held controllers. Of the latter, the type with a battery compartment is useful, provided that the cells fitting into the compartment will give the correct operating voltage.

If possible, the receiver circuit is built on a circuit-board small enough to fit inside the case of the radio or player. **A piece of Blutack or a Sticky Fixer is often a good way to hold the board in place.** The receiver circuit is operated from the battery supply of the radio, which is normally in the range 6V to 12V, which is suitable for this purpose. **Take special care that no conductive part of the board can make contact with conductive parts of the circuit of the instrument.** Check

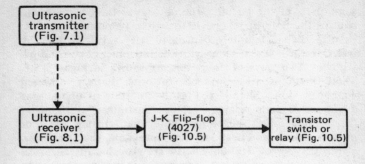

Fig. 11.2
Ultra-sonic on/off control for a radio set or tape-player.
For an infra-red system, the transmitter is Fig. 7.2(b)
or Fig. 7.3, and the receiver is Fig. 8.2 or Fig. 8.3.

that **closing the case does not force previously separated parts into contact.** The ultra-sonic transducer or the light sensor may be fixed to the outside of the case with adhesive tape or Sticky Fixers.

If you are building a sequential pulse system, it may be necessary to include circuitry to eliminate contact bounce. For the sake of simplicity try using a simple button or switch first but, if there are problems with contact bounce, use the circuit of Figure 5.6a. If your system uses infra-red, another solution is to use an ordinary button, followed by the short high-intensity pulse transmitter of Figure 7.3.

Other on/off switching projects, all of which may be realized with virtually the same circuits include:

(2) *Tape player:* Exactly as above.

(3) *Battery powered toy vehicles:* On/off control motor (including reversing), lights, hooter etc. Steering is more difficult unless you have adequate mechanical skill. Provides hours of fun for a child.

(4) *Model railways:* Controlling the locomotive, points, signal lights etc.

196

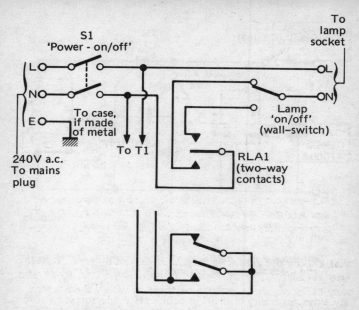

Fig. 11.3 Wiring a lamp to be turned on or off remotely or at a wall-switch.
Inset: alternative relay with two 1-way contacts.

(5) *Table lamp:* Useful for invalids and the elderly.

(6) *Porch lamp:* To switch it on from the garden gate, if there is a long dark path from gate to porch. Figure 11.3 shows how to wire the light so that it may be controlled manually also.

(7) *Electronic flash:* A remote flash is useful for background lighting and when photographing large interiors.

(8) *Solenoid operated devices:* A reasonable amount of motive power may be applied remotely by making use of a solenoid. Applications include operating the shutter of a camera (useful for nature photographers), opening or closing windows, operating bolts, and other functions limited only

197

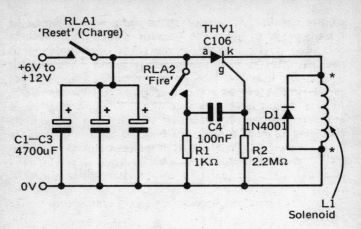

Fig. 11.4

Delivering a very high current to a solenoid. The leads to the solenoid may be extended at the points marked *.

by your ingenuity. In its inactive state the soft-iron core is only partly inside the solenoid. When a large current is passed through the coil the core is drawn into the core forcibly. It is this action that is used to provide the motive power. If possible, the mechanism should be designed so that the core falls out of the coil (or is returned by a spring) ready for a repeat action. A relatively large current is required for a strong positive action. Figure 11.4 shows a battery-powered circuit in which a charge is built up in high-capacitance capacitors and then rapidly discharged through the coil by triggering a thyristor into conduction.

A few of the projects listed above involve switching mains currents. The circuit shown in Figure 10.5 is the basis for most systems of this type. It is suggested that you build this circuit using an ultra-sonic receiver, as shown, or substitute the infra-red receiver of Figure 8.2 or Figure 8.3. The chief point to consider during planning and construction is that the leads to the relay contacts and to the primary coil of the transformer are at mains voltage. **Exposed parts and wires must not be allowed to come into contact** with the wiring of the control circuits. All wires carrying mains voltage should be **thick enough to carry the currents required** to drive the controlled device. Similarly, the **relay contacts should be rated to carry at least the current required. A stout case** is essential; it is preferable to **buy a case** specifically made for electronics devices rather than to try to improvise a case from a sandwich-box or biscuit-tin. The case may be of metal or plastic construction. If it is metal, **a firm connection must be made between the case and the earth line of the mains.** Ensure that **no live parts of the circuit are able to come into contact** with the case. On the whole a good-quality plastic case is to be preferred, except where the case is liable to physical damage.

Projects involving mains are not recommended for beginners.

On/off and volume control for a radio set or tape player
This is a slightly more complicated project, though is still limited to switching by relays. True analogue control of volume and other functions is too complex for a first project. Ultra-sound or infra-red are the obvious choices for the transmission link. If you are building this as an extension of the on/off controller described above, it is simpler to use a sequential pulse system. You can then use the same transmitter.

There are two methods of sequential pulse control. In one (Fig. 11.5), successive stages are: on, change volume, off. A change in volume produces a stepped increase until maximum volume is reached; the next change after that reduces volume to the minimum. This circuit is rather slow to use, but has the merit of simplicity and low cost. **Note that it requires a cut in the loudspeaker lead, which might invalidate the manufacturer's guarantee.**

The on/off function operates by disconnecting the loudspeaker. The change in volume operates by switching one of more resistors into series with the loudspeaker. Relays are wired so that the contacts are closed when the coils are *not* energised. Outputs from the decoder go high in turn each time a pulse is received, so *opening* the contacts. When RLAO is open the sound is muted. When one or the other relays is

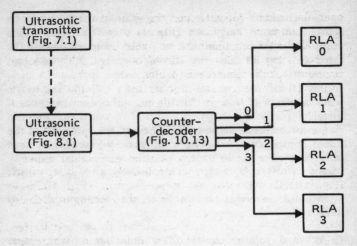

Fig.11.5
Ultra-sonic volume control for a radio set or tape-player.
For an infra-red system, the transmitter is Fig. 7.2(b)
or Fig. 7.3, and the receiver is Fig. 8.2 or Fig. 8.3.

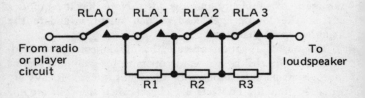

Fig. 11.6
Wiring relays and resistors into the loudspeaker circuit.

open the volume depends upon the value of the resistor thus introduced into the circuit (Fig. 11.6). The exact values required for the resistors must be found by trial. For a starting point, try R1=22 ohm, R2=47 ohm, and R3=100 ohm, assuming that the speaker is an 8-ohm one.

Pin 10 of the counter-decoder i.c. (IC1, Fig. 10.13) is wired to pin 6 of IC2, so that the counter resets when stage 4 is reached.

Other projects can be based on the same principles as the one described above. Resistors switched by relays can be used to control the speed of toy vehicles and model railways. Direction of travel can be controlled by a reversing switch (Fig. 10.22). Though the stepper motor (Figs 10.36 to 10.39) is often preferable, simple relay switching of ordinary motors has many applications in robotics.

The above are just a few suggestions to get you started. After you have built the first few projects and have become experienced in the general principles of remote control you will be able to add and adapt many other of the circuit modules described in this book. We hope that this book will help you design novel and useful remote control systems that will enhance many aspects of your life.

Appendix A

DATA FOR THE CONSTRUCTOR

Transistors, diodes and regulators

Diagrams of terminal connections of all types mentioned in this book appear in Figures A1. In these diagrams the connections are shown as viewed from the *underside* of the device, except for the diodes, which are shown in side view.

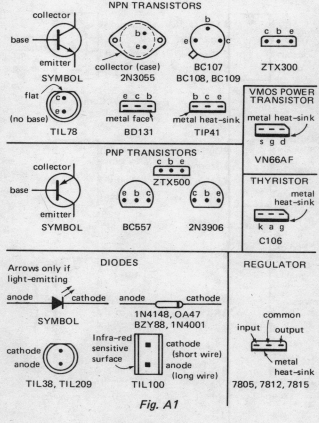

Fig. A1

Integrated circuits

Diagrams of terminal connections of the most frequently used types mentioned in this book appear in Figures A2. In these diagrams the connections are shown as viewed *from above* when the device is mounted on a circuit-board. The connections for the following i.c.s are shown elsewhere in the book: in Figure 6.9, page 70, 490; in Figure 9.4, page 131, 922; and in Figure 10.17, page 160, 4028, 4514, 4515, 7442, 74154.

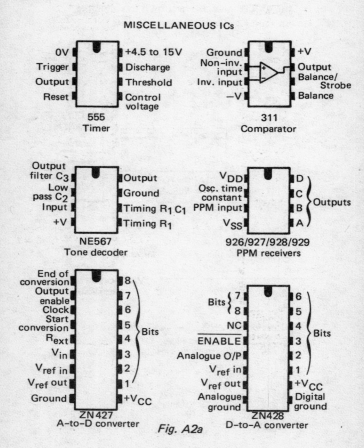

MISCELLANEOUS ICs

555 Timer

311 Comparator

NE567 Tone decoder

926/927/928/929 PPM receivers

ZN427 A-to-D converter

ZN428 D-to-A converter

Fig. A2a

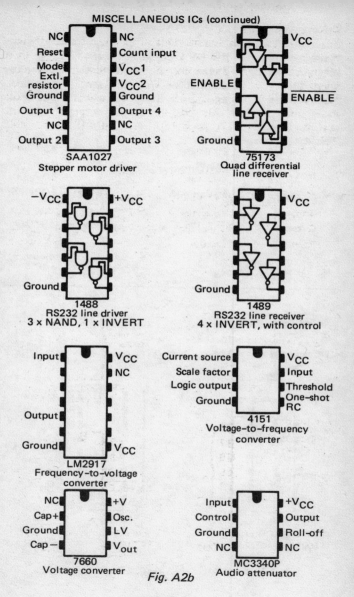

MISCELLANEOUS ICs (continued)

NC	NC
Reset	Count input
Mode	$V_{CC}1$
Extl. resistor	$V_{CC}2$
Ground	Ground
Output 1	Output 4
NC	NC
Output 2	Output 3

SAA1027
Stepper motor driver

75173
Quad differential
line receiver

ENABLE

$\overline{ENABLE}$

V_{CC}

Ground

$-V_{CC}$ $+V_{CC}$

Ground

1488
RS232 line driver
3 x NAND, 1 x INVERT

V_{CC}

Ground

1489
RS232 line receiver
4 x INVERT, with control

Input	V_{CC}
	NC
Output	
Ground	V_{CC}

LM2917
Frequency–to–voltage
converter

Current source	V_{CC}
Scale factor	Input
Logic output	Threshold
Ground	One-shot RC

4151
Voltage–to–frequency
converter

NC	+V
Cap+	Osc.
Ground	LV
Cap −	V_{out}

7660
Voltage converter

Input	$+V_{CC}$
Control	Output
Ground	Roll-off
NC	NC

MC3340P
Audio attenuator

Fig. A2b

205

OPERATIONAL AMPLIFIERS

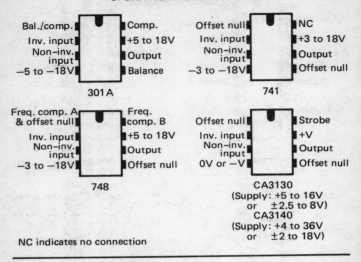

301 A

Bal./comp. | Comp.
Inv. input | +5 to 18V
Non-inv. input | Output
−5 to −18V | Balance

741

Offset null | NC
Inv. input | +3 to 18V
Non-inv. input | Output
−3 to −18V | Offset null

748

Freq. comp. A & offset null | Freq. comp. B
Inv. input | +5 to 18V
Non-inv. input | Output
−3 to −18V | Offset null

CA3130
(Supply: +5 to 16V or ±2.5 to 8V)
CA3140
(Supply: +4 to 36V or ±2 to 18V)

Offset null | Strobe
Inv. input | +V
Non-inv. input | Output
0V or −V | Offset null

NC indicates no connection

CMOS ICs

Q indicates an output

Q̄ is the inverted output

NC indicates no connection

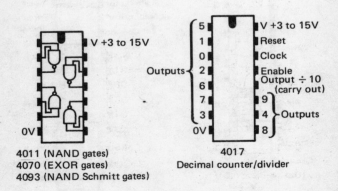

4011 (NAND gates)
4070 (EXOR gates)
4093 (NAND Schmitt gates)

4017
Decimal counter/divider

V +3 to 15V

5, 1, 0, 2, 6, 7, 3, 0V — Outputs

V +3 to 15V
Reset
Clock
Enable
Output ÷ 10 (carry out)
9, 4, 8 — Outputs

Fig. A2c

206

CMOS ICs (continued)

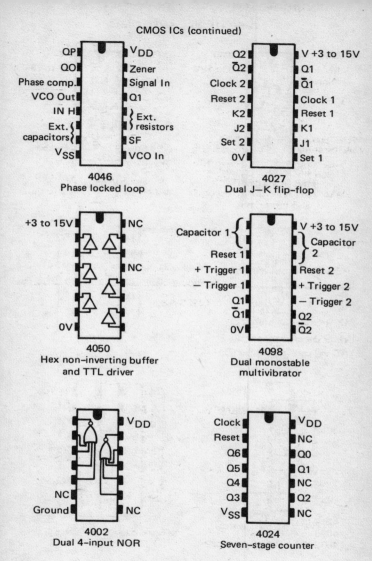

Fig. A2d

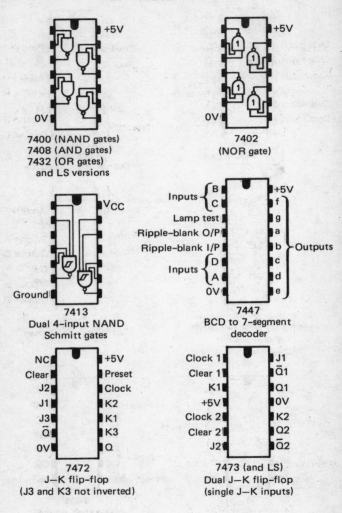

7400 (NAND gates)
7408 (AND gates)
7432 (OR gates)
and LS versions

7402
(NOR gate)

7413
Dual 4-input NAND
Schmitt gates

7447
BCD to 7-segment
decoder

7472
J–K flip-flop
(J3 and K3 not inverted)

7473 (and LS)
Dual J–K flip-flop
(single J–K inputs)

Fig. A2e

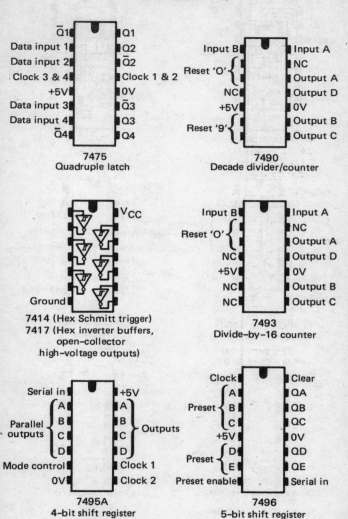

7475
Quadruple latch

7490
Decade divider/counter

7414 (Hex Schmitt trigger)
**7417 (Hex inverter buffers,
open-collector
high-voltage outputs)**

7493
Divide-by-16 counter

7495A
4-bit shift register

7496
5-bit shift register

Fig. A2f

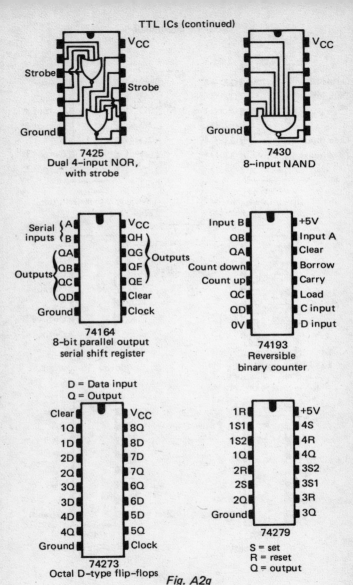

7425
Dual 4-input NOR,
with strobe

7430
8-input NAND

74164
8-bit parallel output
serial shift register

74193
Reversible
binary counter

74273
Octal D-type flip-flops

74279

S = set
R = reset
Q = output

Fig. A2g

210

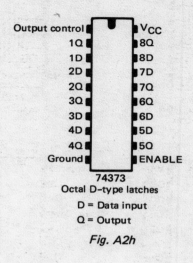

74373
Octal D-type latches
D = Data input
Q = Output

Fig. A2h

Appendix B

USEFUL BOOKS FOR THE BEGINNER

Easy introduction to electronic theory

Enjoying Electronics by Owen Bishop, published by Cambridge University Press, 1983

A practical introduction to electronic circuits by Martin Hartley-Jones, published by Cambridge University Press, 1977 — not quite as easy but goes into greater depth, and is well written.

Project building
All the following books are published by Bernard Babani (publishing) Ltd:

227, *Beginners Guide to Building Electronic Projects* by R. A. Penfold.

BP48, *Electronic Projects for Beginners* by F. G. Rayer.

BP97, *IC Projects for Beginners* by F. G. Rayer.

BP107, *30 Solderless Breadboard Projects — Book 1* by R. A. Penfold

BP113, *30 Solderless Breadboard Projects — Book 2* by R. A. Penfold

BP110, *How to Get Your Electronic Projects Working* by R. A. Penfold

BP121, *How to Design and Make Your Own PCBs* by R. A. Penfold.

Computer interfacing
These books, published by Bernard Babani (publishing) Ltd, go into the details more fully than has been possible in this book, and some include useful tips on programming for input and output.

BP124, *Easy Add-on Projects for Spectrum, ZX81 and Ace* by Owen Bishop.

Appendix C

SUPPLIERS

Maplin Electronic Supplies Ltd, P.O. Box 3, Rayleigh, Essex SS6 8LR. Telephone Enquiries (0702) 552911.
Supply most components used in this book, as well as kits and p.c.b.s for the radio control transmitter and receiver, the mains transceiver, and the stepper motor driver.

Electromail, P.O. Box 33, Corby, Northants NN17 9EL. Telephone Orders (0536) 204555.

Appendix D

POWER SUPPLIES

Many, if not most of the projects described in this book can be operated from batteries. Batteries have the advantage in portable equipment, particularly hand-held controllers. For CMOS including CMOS versions of TTL, with its very low power requirements, a small 9V battery such as a PP3 can provide power for several weeks of operation. Standard and low-power TTL circuits are designed to operate on a 5V supply, which is not convenient to obtain from batteries. However, they seem to work equally well on 6V. Standard TTL requires more current than CMOS, so may be unsuitable for powering by batteries if there are several complex i.c.s. One solution is to replace the standard TTL (7400) by the low power Schottky range (74LS00), as has been done already in several circuits in this book. Indeed, some of the TTL i.c.s are not available in the standard range.

For long periods of operation, for extensive circuits, and where portability is not essential, a mains power pack is preferable. Power pack kits are available, but it is not a difficult matter for a person with a little constructional experience to build a mains power supply. This can often be accommodated on the same circuit board as the remote control circuit. **Care must be taken that parts at mains voltages can not come into contact with parts at low voltages. Circuits must be carefully checked before connecting to the mains. When testing mains-powered circuits, it is recommended that power is taken from a mains socket with a residual current circuit breaker.**

Figure D1 is a circuit for a 12V stabilized supply. The transformer T1 is rated at 100VA and has a 15V secondary winding. The 15V a.c. is rectified by the bridge of diodes D1–D4. These may be individual rectifying diodes rated at 5A or more, or a bridge rectifier also rated at 5A or more. The rectified 15V d.c. is smoothed by capacitor C1, which should be rated for a working voltage of at least 15V. The stabilizing circuit consists of R1, TR1 and the zener diode D5. TR1 is a power transistor and should be bolted to a heat sink. Final

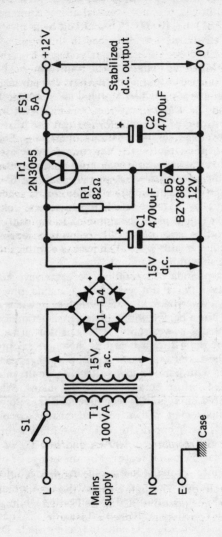

Fig. D1 12-volt stabilised power supply, delivering up to 5A.

smoothing of the supply is by C2, also at least 15V working voltage. Although it is not essential, it is recommended that a 5A fuse (FS1) be fitted. This circuit will produce ample power for all the devices described in this book. The design can be modified for other output voltages by substituting a zener diode of other voltages. The transformer chosen should have a secondary winding of output voltage slightly more than the required stabilized voltage. If a voltage lower than 12V is used, or the current requirements are less than 5A, the power rating of the transformer can be correspondingly reduced. For example, for a 6V output and a maximum of 2A current, the power rating of the transformer need only be 12VA. It is worth considering this point because a transformer with lower power rating is cheaper and is smaller. A wide range of p.c.b. mounting transformers is available, rated at 12, 6 or 3VA. These are inexpensive and take up little space, making them specially suitable for compact equipment.

For optimum operation TTL requires a regulated power supply; the circuit of Figure D2 employs a voltage regulator to

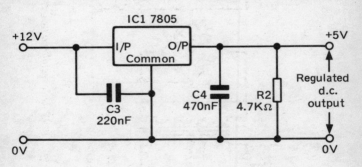

Fig. D2 5V regulated power supply for TTL, up to 1A.

produce a well regulated 5V supply from a stabilized supply of higher voltage. The figure shows the regulator receiving a 12V supply, but operates just as well on any voltage from 7V to 25V. The regulator may need a heat sink.

219

Notes

Please note following is a list of other titles that are available in our range of Radio, Electronics and Computer books.

These should be available from all good Booksellers, Radio Component Dealers and Mail Order Companies.

However, should you experience difficulty in obtaining any title in your area, then please write directly to the Publisher enclosing payment to cover the cost of the book plus adequate postage.

If you would like a complete catalogue of our entire range of Radio, Electronics and Computer Books then please send a Stamped Addressed Envelope to:

BERNARD BABANI (publishing) LTD
THE GRAMPIANS
SHEPHERDS BUSH ROAD
LONDON W6 7NF
ENGLAND